W9-CXW-349

/95

Shelburne Museum:
A Guide to the Collections

A Guide to the Collections

Shelburne Museum

© 1993 Shelburne Museum, Inc.,
Shelburne, Vermont
All rights reserved

ISBN: 0-939384-19-1

Published by Shelburne Museum, Inc.
Post Office Box 10
Shelburne, Vermont 05482
802/985-3346

The Shelburne Museum is a place of the imagination, reflecting its founder's dream of presenting early American life and culture in a distinctive way. The result is an eclectic collection of collections which integrates art and history, period homes and community buildings, and traditional museum galleries.

The Museum's founder, Electra Havemeyer Webb, was inspired by the desire to preserve and interpret the cultural legacy of America's ordinary people. She envisioned a museum that would deepen visitor appreciation for the objects of everyday lives. It is our hope that this guide to the collections will further this goal and be enjoyed by our visitors, enhancing the museum experience, bringing a sense of continuity to the great depth and breadth of the collections, and providing a means for later reflection and recollection.

We welcome you to the Shelburne Museum, and hope that your visit is enjoyable and that you return often.

David Sheldon, Executive Director
Brian Alexander, Director

Welcome

Table of Contents

Suggested Tours

Museum Notes

Index

Museum Map

Credits

Shelburne Museum's mission is to preserve, interpret and develop for public understanding collections of early American arts, architecture and artifacts. Comprising a rich resource of material culture, these nationally significant collections document the artistic, agricultural and community traditions of American's regional cultures, with an emphasis on New England and Vermont.

Shelburne Museum: A Guide to the Collections describes and illustrates these important resources for understanding America's past. It is designed to be used while visiting the Museum, or at home for research and to plan future visits.

Major collection areas are described in a series of short essays authored by Shelburne curators and educators. Ranging in subject from fine arts to woodworking tools, each essay addresses the collection's historical significance and the breadth and depth of Shelburne's holdings. Exhibit buildings are also described in essays that highlight notable architectural features and describe former uses of the Muscum's historical structures.

The guide also includes an overview of the scope and history of the Museum, thematic tour suggestions, and notes describing the Museum's efforts in the interpretation and preservation of its collections.

Challenged to describe the unique and eclectic museum she had created, Shelburne's founder, Electra Havemeyer Webb, advanced the phrase "a collection of collections." Nestled in the Champlain Valley of Vermont, the Shelburne Museum today is home to thirty-seven exhibit buildings housing some eighty thousand objects that span three centuries. At first glance the Museum resembles a well-preserved historic village, but on closer inspection its diversity becomes evident. An Adirondack-style hunting lodge sits within range of a turn-of-the-century side paddlewheel steamboat, that in turn borders a collection of 18th- and 19th-century community buildings and historic houses. Some of these architectural treasures contain

Electra Havemeyer Webb, 1888-1960.

exhibits documenting the historical period and function that their exteriors suggest, while other buildings—many of which were also collected for their architectural legacies—serve as gallery spaces for such collections as folk sculpture, quilts, hatboxes, circus figures, and American and European paintings. At Shelburne, elements of both art and history are fused into a lively combination that welcomes visitors with wide-ranging interests.

The central vision that unifies this rich assortment originated with the Museum's founder, Electra Havemeyer Webb. She was fascinated by the unexpected and often unintended beauty of utilitarian objects. In a lifetime of passionate collecting, she chose those objects made for both home and workplace that best exemplified the ingenuity and craftsmanship of the pre-industrial era. When she decided to exhibit her collections in a public museum, she sought an approach that had not been tried by others also establishing museums at this time. Electra Webb chose to exhibit 18th- and 19th-century objects in historic structures of the period, but without the intention to recreate a literal historical moment or period. Instead, the variety of buildings would serve as galleries where the collections could be enjoyed in a friendly, informal atmosphere.

The insights that guided Electra Webb's devel-

Horace and Electra with their father, Henry Osborne Havemeyer. (Courtesy of James Watson Webb, Jr.)

opment of the Shelburne Museum in 1947 had been honed since her childhood. Daughter of fine art collectors Henry Osborne and Louisine Elder Havemeyer, Electra had accompanied her parents as they traveled to galleries, museums and artists' studios in pursuit of paintings, sculpture and decorative arts. The New York City home in which she was raised was not only a setting for fine and decorative arts, but also a meeting place for painters, architects, sculptors, musicians and editors.

By 1907, eighteen-year-old Electra Havemeyer had decided that she would use the legacy recently inherited from her father to build a collection of her own. Three years later she married James Watson Webb, grandson of William Henry Vanderbilt, and began to fill their

Portrait of Electra and her mother, Louisine Elder Havemeyer, painted by Mary Cassatt, 1895. (Private collection.)

Electra and James Watson Webb with their children, (left to right) Lila, Sam, Electra and James Jr. (Courtesy of James Watson Webb, Jr.)

homes with American antiques. Over the next thirty years she raised five children, managed households in Long Island, New York City and Shelburne, Vermont, traveled widely, and worked closely with the American Red Cross. All the while she pursued her interest in collecting.

Electra Webb's appetite for American antiques was voracious. Living rooms, attics and even indoor tennis courts became crowded: "The rooms were

Interior of the Webb's Westbury, Long Island home, 1935. (Courtesy of James Watson Webb, Jr.)

over-furnished.... Then the closets and the attics were filled. I just couldn't let good pieces go by—china, porcelain, pottery, pewter, glass, dolls, quilts, cigar store Indians, eagles, folk art. They all seemed to appeal to me." In 1947, when her husband's retirement enabled the couple to make Vermont their primary residence, she was able to realize a life-long dream: the creation of a museum in which to share her collections with the public.

Dr. William Seward Webb at Shelburne Farms.

The catalyst for the project was the need to find a home for the carriages that had belonged to her father-in-law. In the first year, Electra Webb bought land near the center of the town of Shelburne that contained a red brick dwelling known locally as the Weed House. This would provide galleries for glass, silver, ceramics and dolls. But there still remained the challenge of the carriages. Electra and Watson Webb had admired old buildings they saw

"Weed House", Shelburne, Vt.

in their travels through the New England countryside. One such building, an unusual horseshoe-shaped barn, would do the job well, and so Mrs. Webb set a team of carpenters to construct a replica from salvaged timbers and slates. As word of her project spread, other buildings were offered by people hoping to

Horseshoe Barn, built at the Museum from 1947 to 1949.

preserve them. Shelburne's selectmen donated the old town barn, and with the creative twist that was to characterize her work, Electra Webb adapted the building to exhibit her collection of textiles.

From the start, the Shelburne Museum was assembled as a vast, three-dimensional collage of buildings and collections. Buildings were painstakingly moved to the site and refurbished. In some cases, such as the General Store and Blacksmith Shop, the buildings were moved in one piece. In other cases—the Covered Bridge and the Stone Cot-

Blacksmith Shop being transported to the Museum on January 17, 1956.

tage, for example—elements were carefully numbered, disassembled, moved and assembled again.

Variety as a theme was expressed in the way collections were exhibited, and in the range of the collections themselves. In some installations, objects were selected to

Stone Cottage in preparation for its removal from South Burlington, Vt. to the Museum in 1949.

Interior view, Vermont House.

create settings evocative of a particular period and subject, such as the 19th-century sea captain's home in the Vermont House. In other exhibitions, collections remained together, serving as a three-dimensional encyclopedia of textiles in the Hat and Fragrance Textile Gallery, for example, or of ceramics, glass, pewter and dolls in the Variety Unit.

In collecting, Electra Webb shared ideas and interests with other pioneers in the field of American folk and decorative arts. Like Abby Aldrich Rockefeller, she purchased folk art through Edith Halpert's Downtown Gallery in New York. She corresponded and exchanged

Ceramic teapots.

visits with Henry Francis du Pont as he assembled a peerless collection of American decorative arts and gradually turned his family home in Delaware into the Winterthur Museum. When she decided to expand her collection of paintings to fill a fine art gallery at the Museum, she consulted Maxim Karolik, whose collection of American paintings graced the Boston Museum of Fine Arts.

Occasionally, Mrs. Webb acquired and displayed complete collections developed by others.

The Dorset House in its original location in East Dorset, Vt., 1952.

Woodworking tools collected by Frank Wildung became the core of the exhibition on tools and trades in the Shaker Shed, and the Dorset House was acquired to provide a suitable home for the seminal collection of wildfowl decoys assembled by Joel Barber.

Decoy exhibit, Dorset House.

In some years as many as three or four structures were added to the Museum; in 1955, the Blacksmith Shop, Sawyer's Cabin and Prentis House were

The *Ticonderoga*, just inland from Lake Champlain, being readied for its one and three-quarters mile journey to the Museum.

moved intact, and the steamboat *Ticonderoga* made her legendary overland voyage to the Museum grounds. By 1960, twenty-three historic structures had been moved to Shelburne. A scale model with miniature replicas helped to plan locations and landscaping. The newly constructed gallery of portraits, marine paintings and genre scenes, that opened in 1960, was the last project of Electra and James Watson Webb. Their deaths came within the year only months apart.

It was then that J. Watson Webb, Jr. moved from California to take up leadership of the Museum. Over the next seventeen years he implemented, interpreted and amplified his mother's vision. Among major projects of this era, the Beach Hunting Lodge and Gallery

James Watson Webb, Jr. (Courtesy of James Watson Webb, Jr.)

were completed. The final design of the 550-foot-long Circus Parade building was approved, and the building was filled with a magical combination of miniature circus figures and full-size posters and carousel figures. The private railroad car was acquired and its beautifully appointed interior carefully restored and furnished.

During this period the Electra Havemeyer Webb Memorial Building was specially constructed to exhibit rooms from Mrs. Webb's New York City home. Mrs. Webb had intended to bring to the Museum

Interior, Electra Havemeyer Webb Memorial Building.

the collection of European and Oriental art inherited from her parents. While the formal elegance of rooms furnished with paintings by Rembrandt, Degas, Monet and Manet, as well as bronzes, porcelain, and Oriental wallpaper seems to contrast in style with the rest of the Museum, there are clear connections, not only biographical, but philosophical. Perhaps most important is the message that art is meant above all to be enjoyed as part of daily life.

The Round Barn's silo arrives by helicopter in 1986.

Today, with widespread interest in American folk art and in the lives of ordinary people, the Museum's collections and programs continue to expand. Moving buildings is now a rare occurrence—the arrival of the Round Barn's silo by helicopter in l986 was the first such event in over a decade. Instead, the Museum's team of highly skilled staff members combines forces to preserve these resources for future generations and to make them broadly accessible to all audiences. The collections continue to grow through gifts and purchases that complement current holdings. Together they further enrich the Museum's legacy of folk, fine and decorative arts and artifacts that evoke the American traditions of craftsmanship and ingenuity.

Building Directory

Apothecary Shop

The Apothecary Shop, attached to the General Store, was constructed at the Museum in 1959. Inside, the display shelves, pill press and other professional tools create the appearance of a druggist's shop in operation between 1870 and 1900. Displayed in its front windows are symbols of the apothecary trade: glass vessels containing colored fluids, with red representing arterial blood and blue representing venous blood.

Prior to the Civil War, druggists gathered and dried herbs, then prepared them for medicinal use through grinding or distillation. The resulting materials were combined with sugar, lard, alcohol and other substances to create tablets, ointments and elixirs. While these practices continued into the late 19th century, druggists gradually responded to an ever-greater demand for patent medicines as customers began to prefer brightly labeled cure-alls over herbal remedies. Passage of the Pure Food and Drug Act in 1906 marked the end of the apothecary shop and the beginning of the modern drugstore.

Much of the contents of this apothecary exhibit was salvaged from New England pharmacies that were closing in the early decades of the 20th century. The main room contains dried herbs, spices, drugs, and labeled glass apothecary bottles of the earlier period, as well as later patent medicines, medical equipment, cosmetics and a collection of barbers' razors. The compounding room, containing a brick hearth, copper distilleries and percolators, was designed following an illustration found in the 1871 edition of Parishe's *Treatise on Pharmacy*.

The Beach Lodge and Gallery are log buildings designed to resemble an Adirondack hunting camp. The buildings were constructed on the present site in 1960 using timber from the Museum founders' 50,000-acre northern New York preserve, "Nehasane." The intent was to create an environment distinctly different from the rest of the Museum by excavating a shallow basin and surrounding it with Vermont sandstone sheltered by spruce, hemlock and cedar trees. The buildings are named for William and Marie Beach, hunting companions of Mr. and Mrs. Webb and donors of many of the exhibits contained therein.

The Beach Lodge is decorated in the style of an Adirondack camp and includes hunting trophies and handmade boats the like of which were valued as personal momentos of high adventure. Adirondack-style furniture, fashioned of tree limbs or animal antlers, was often made for camp owners by local craftspeople. This rustic decorating style also reflects the late 19th- and 20th-century interest in such eth-

nographic material as American Indian clothing, baskets and wood carvings.

The Beach Gallery exhibits paintings, prints and bronzes by artists whose work explores the theme of the disappearing American wilderness. Arthur Fitzwilliam Tait produced countless scenes of American wild life and sold many paintings to Currier and Ives to be copied as inexpensive lithographs. Sydney Laurence, a western adventurer, depicted Alaskan scenery with an awe for its "startling beauty." Carl Rungius, a hunting companion of both Theodore Roosevelt and William Beach, frequently depicted big game animals, using mounted trophies as models. Bronzes depicting western subjects are also exhibited in the gallery as are additional Adirondack-style furniture and some of the Museum's best examples of American Indian beadwork.

BEACH LODGE AND GALLERY

Blacksmith Shop

The Blacksmith Shop, a one-room brick structure built about 1800, and its later frame addition, originally stood near the railroad tracks in the village of Shelburne, Vermont. Little is known of its early occupancy, but John Dubuc is recorded as having operated a blacksmith shop there in 1869. The building was later occupied by a succession of craftspeople until abandoned in 1935.

The building was acquired by the Museum in 1955 and moved to its present site. In preparation for the move the building was fitted with a footing of reinforced concrete, braced internally, jacked up, and rolled onto the bed of a twenty-four-ton trailer. It was then transported twenty-four hundred feet down Route 7 to the Museum grounds. The building was re-outfitted with blacksmith and wheelwright tools acquired from a variety of local sources and opened in 1956 as the Museum's first working exhibit.

Communities of the 18th and 19th centuries depended heavily on the village blacksmith as a primary source for tools, utensils, agricultural implements, architectural hardware, vehicle parts and many other items. Many blacksmiths also served as farriers, not only manufacturing shoes for horses and oxen, but fitting them to the animals as well.

In larger communities the blacksmith often worked in conjunction with the wheelwright in the manufacture and repair of vehicle wheels. Although combination blacksmith-and-wheelwright shops persisted into the 20th century, their focus gradually changed from manufacture of one-of-a-kind items to the repair of factory-produced goods. Eventually, with the ever-increasing availability of products and the advent of the automobile, both blacksmiths and wheelwrights were rendered obsolete.

The Shelburne Museum Blacksmith Shop represents the trade as practiced in the early 20th century. The wood-and-leather bellows rests in its customary position by the forge, though it is replaced in actual use by a more efficient, electrically powered blower. This was particularly helpful for the many smiths of this period who found themselves working alone because of the breakdown of the apprentice system. An electrically operated trip-hammer mounted near the forge also enabled the smith to handle larger work without assistance.

The design for the Circus Building was conceived in the 1950s to meet the requirements of exhibiting a complete carousel and a five-hundred-foot-long miniature circus parade. A large horseshoe-shaped structure was envisioned to house the parade, with the carousel to be set between the arms of the horseshoe. To dramatize the shape and placement of the building, huge boulders were brought in to elevate the foundation and serve as the base for a rock garden. The structure was completed in 1965.

The most unusual feature of this spruce and cedar building is the curved five-hundred-foot-long grand hallway. This houses the Roy Arnold miniature circus parade, carved on a scale of one inch to one foot. Along the opposite wall are forty carousel figures, chariots and painted panels made by the

Gustav Dentzel Carousel Company of Philadelphia. These are set against a backdrop of a collection of lithographed circus posters.

Foyers at either end of the building contain additional circus exhibits. The west entrance foyer features the three thousand-piece Kirk Bros. Miniature Circus and a life-sized carved wooden ringmaster to welcome visitors. The east foyer exhibits brightly painted circus wagons, decorative circus carvings, and the miniature Sig Sautelle canal boat circus.

The Covered Bridge was built in 1845 to span the Lamoille River in Cambridge, Vermont. Measuring 168 feet in length, with two vehicle lanes and a footpath, it is an impressive example of the engineering principles and bridge builder's craft practiced during the mid-19th century.

Through practical experience builders had learned that a roof both protected open bridges from severe weather and added structural stability. As a further benefit, enclosed sides shielded farm animals from frightening views. The arch truss bridge, of which this is an example, was patented by Vermont inventor Theodore Burr in 1804. Great arches, bolted to a framework of multiple king-post trusses, reached from one bank to the other. It was an improvement that permitted longer spans.

The Covered Bridge was dismantled and moved to the Museum grounds in 1949, where today the beams still bear their identifying numbers for reconstruction. The bridge was integrated into the landscape plan by situating it above a man-made pond and served for many years as the Museum's entrance. When automobile traffic proved too taxing, the Museum's entrance was relocated and the bridge was retired from active duty.

The Dorset House, built about 1832 in East Dorset, Vermont, is an excellent example of Greek Revival architecture. Design motifs from classical civilization were widely popular in America in the early 19th century because they symbolized to American citizens their link with the democracies of ancient Greece and Rome.

The house is constructed in a substantial but unpretentious style. The facade is dominated by a massive cornice, and slabs of marble are used as a veneer for the foundation and porches. Its two and a half-story, front-gable main block is flanked by cross-gabled wings giving the building classical balance and symmetry.

Welcome Allen of Dorset built the house for his children, Florenze and Lucia. Their families used the side doors as entrances to separate living quarters within the house. Welcome Allen and later his son Florenze were proprietors of a foundry where they cast iron stove plates, plow points and kettles. Unlike most homes of the era, the Dorset House was built

without open fireplace hearths, as the family used closed iron stoves for all heating.

The Dorset House was dismantled and moved to the Museum in 1953 to serve as an exhibit space for the wildfowl decoy collection, which grew to include working and decorative decoys and miniature bird carvings. Paintings and prints of hunting scenes and American birds, including hand-colored engravings by John James Audubon, complement the carvings.

Dutton House

The Dutton House was built in Cavendish, Vermont, in 1782. The building style now known as "saltbox" was widely used in the 17th century, and continued to be popular throughout the 18th and into the 19th centuries. The term "saltbox" refers to the asymmetrical roof line resembling the profile of an early wooden salt container. The extended roof most likely faced north on the house's original site, to diminish the impact of cold winter winds, while the bank of windows on the opposite exterior wall faced south, collecting warmth from the sun. The dentil molding on the cornice, copied from a house in Alburg, Vermont, was added after the house came to the Museum.

Like most homes of its era, the Dutton House served many different purposes through the generations. Salmon Dutton, who emigrated from Massachusetts in 1781, built the house as his family residence and place of business. He worked as a road surveyor, owned a toll road, and served the town of Cavendish as selectman, justice of the peace and treasurer. His descendants, who occupied the house until 1900, added wings which served as a store and inn and provided housing for mill workers.

In the late 1940s Dutton's great-great-grandson, Redfield Proctor, gave the house, which had been empty for over forty years, to the Vermont Historical Society. However, Vermont Highway Department road-widening plans threatened the structure, and the Society in turn offered it to the Shelburne Museum. This was the first dwelling brought to the Museum property.

Relocation to Shelburne in 1950 required that the house be entirely dismantled. In the process, fragments of original stenciled wall ornaments were exposed. The dismantling of the house was completed in thirteen and a half working days, and the pieces were trucked to the Museum where the shell was re-erected. The roof was ready for shingles eighteen days later. The stencils were carefully reproduced on the newly plastered walls. The house was then furnished with rural Vermont and New England furniture and household objects of the 18th and 19th centuries arranged in room settings to suggest a family's accumulation over several generations.

The Electra Havemeyer Webb Memorial Building, built between 1960 and 1967, was constructed of new materials on its present site. Copied in part from a farmhouse in Orwell, Vermont, it is a fine example of fully developed Greek Revival architecture. The massive Ionic columns of the two-story porch echo a Greek temple facade. The interior was designed to accommodate the replication of six rooms from Mr. & Mrs. J. Watson Webb's Manhattan apartment.

Electra Webb had proposed to bring her collection of European and Asian paintings, furniture and decorative objects to Shelburne as a memorial to her parents, collectors Henry O. and Louisine Havemeyer. Following her death in 1960, her children wanted to fulfill her wish. J. Watson Webb, Jr., then president of the Museum, suggested moving entire rooms from his parents' apartment so that their arrangements of furniture and decorative arts could be preserved intact.

Unlike the Museum's historic houses that provide insight into Electra Webb's interests as a collector, the Memorial building tells something of the forces that influenced her life. Electra Webb fitted out her city quarters with a formal combination of English, European and Asian furniture and decorative objects. Her collection of paintings, including works by Rembrandt, Corot, Manet, Monet and Degas, had come to her from her parents. Family photographs, portraits and memorabilia complete the furnishings on display today.

Gardens and Grounds

Shelburne Museum's gardens and grounds, like its other collections, are meant to offer enjoyment, information, and an opportunity for reflection. Using a scale model and miniatures, Museum founder Electra Havemeyer Webb worked with Long Island landscape designer Umberto Innocenti to plan settings that ultimately determined the placement of buildings, trees, gardens, walkways and in some cases, earth itself. The intent was not to replicate a specific village of years past, but rather to create a setting in which the past could be better understood and enjoyed. Innocenti's taste for uncluttered sweeps of open lawn, panoramic views, and a range of plantings that offer enjoyment throughout the seasons was perfect for Electra Webb's purpose.

The large maples and locust trees, still thriving today on the northern part of the grounds, are among the only significant plantings original to the site. Close to four hundred lilacs—ninety varieties among them—were planted near house foundations, as they have been for centuries in New England. Apple varieties, including New England mainstays McIntosh and Cortlands, enlivened open spaces, while pines, hemlock, spruce, and cedars were moved to the Beach Basin to suggest the forest of the nearby Adirondack Mountains.

Some gardens have a specific function while others merely offer pleasure. The Apothecary herb garden grows traditional medicinal herbs and plants; the garden in the lee of the Hat and Fragrance Textile Gallery contains traditional herbs and plants used to prepare and preserve food, and to dye wool, cotton and linen yarn and fabrics. Meanwhile, both the Pleissner and Bostwick Gardens offer pleasant rest spots in a more formal setting. The Pleissner Garden evokes the atmosphere of painter Odgen Pleissner's gardens in southern Vermont. The Bostwick Garden, designed and maintained in memory of Electra Webb Bostwick, offers a medley of annuals and perennials gracefully framed by dry stone walls of local origin that surround the bronze sculpture *Turtle Baby* by Edith Parsons (1878-1956).

Informal settings with pleasing views, often flanked by fragrant rose bushes are scattered around the Museum's forty-five acres. Wooden benches are placed throughout for visitors' enjoyment.

26

GARDENS AND GROUNDS

The General Store was constructed in 1840 in nearby Shelburne Center, where it served as the village post office for years. Its primary Greek Revival feature is its front-gable orientation, emphasized by a multi-paned triangular window above the second story.

In 1952, the building was moved intact to the Museum on a specially laid railroad track. The first level re-creates a late 19th-century general store. Fully stocked shelves display the variety of goods formerly available for purchase, while smaller adjoining rooms offer a variety of community services. These include a post office, barber shop and tap room. A nineteenth-century apothecary shop is housed in a wing added to the building after it was moved to the Museum grounds.

The building's second story contains collec-

tions of medical equipment, tools and furnishings spanning the first half of the 20th century. Re-created settings include a dentist's laboratory and examining room, and the offices of an eye, ear, nose and throat physician.

Hat and Fragrance Textile Gallery

This building was constructed by Captain Benjamin Harrington as a distillery in Shelburne, Vermont, about 1800. Captain Harrington owned and operated a nearby inn and produced spirits to serve his guests. The building later served as the Shelburne town barn and after a period of disuse, it was given to the Museum in 1947 and moved to its present site.

Constructed of handhewn timbers and rough planks, the barn was used for several years as a storage and workshop space while Museum founder Electra Webb decided how best to renovate the

space as a textile gallery. The interior was remodeled using old materials where possible. The gallery walls were covered with maple, birch and beech veneers in decorative patterns.

The name "Hat and Fragrance" refers to Electra Webb's outstanding collection of hatboxes and to the herbal sachets used to preserve early textiles. Four one-story rooms were added to the original barn to provide space for her collections of quilts, rugs, hatboxes, costumes and shadow boxes of miniatures.

Electra Havemeyer Webb's desire to provide a suitable setting for the carriage collection of her father-in-law, Dr. William Seward Webb, provided the inspiration for founding the Shelburne Museum. She searched Vermont for a building to house these fine carriages and found a unique horseshoe-shaped dairy barn near Georgia, Vermont. When the owner declined to sell the barn, Electra Webb directed her staff to create a copy of the structure. Over a two year period they located, moved and assembled hand-hewn beams from twelve Vermont barns, and stone from two gristmills.

Construction began in May, 1947, and was completed by July, 1949. The massive structure incorporated 745 timbers, posts and braces, 17,000 feet of plank and other boarding, and 9,000 square feet of slate. New clapboards for the exterior were specially

cut to reproduce the markings of an up-and-down saw. The barn has an outside length of 238 1/2 feet and a width of 32 feet.

The core of the exhibit is the collection of forty-seven vehicles used by the Webb family. With the addition of over 150 more wagons, sleighs, coaches, other vehicles and fire equipment from other sources, more exhibit space was needed. The Horseshoe Barn Annex was constructed on its present site in 1957 using a combination of old and new materials.

Horseshoe Barn and Annex

HORSESHOE BARN AND ANNEX

Jail

The Castleton Jail was constructed in 1890 in Castleton, a town in the heart of Vermont's slate quarry district. While slate was often used for paths, low walls and roofing, in this case the exterior walls and floors were constructed of locally abundant slate and reinforced with railroad irons. The dark interior consists of two cells and a jailor's compartment with only a single window to admit light and air. A riveted iron door completes this impregnable structure. In this form, the jail was used for over fifty years.

In 1953, the fifty-ton jail was purchased by the Museum from the town of Castleton for one dollar per ton. Only the roof and gable ends were removed for the sixty-four-mile journey to Shelburne. Special dollies with twenty-four rubber-tired wheels were built to carry the basic structure. A separate steering apparatus and four sets of brakes were needed to maintain control on the steep hills. The move, aided by the Vermont State Police, required three days at speeds varying

from three to seven miles an hour. The most difficult obstacle was the Vergennes underpass of the Rutland Railroad, where the clearance was only five inches.

The stocks and pillory, located in front of the jail, were constructed to recall a form of punishment common in 17th- and early 18th-century New England. Public confinement in such devices was considered an appropriate penalty for offenses such as theft or gambling. The sentence was often carried out in the town square under the scornful gaze of local clergymen and citizens.

The Lighthouse was built in 1871 in Lake Champlain, between Vermont and New York State, to mark the position of three reefs—the Colchester Reef, Colchester Shoals and the Hogback Reef—which threatened ships approaching Burlington from the north.

Increased commerce on the lake in the mid- to late 19th century led the United States Lighthouse Establishment to authorize the building of lighthouses to protect ships in potentially hazardous waterways. In 1869, the Lighthouse Establishment ran a national contest for lighthouse designs. Burlington resident Albert Dow won the contest and his plans were used to construct the lighthouse on Colchester Reef as well as others in the region.

Built to endure strong lake winds, the building's twenty-five-foot square post-and-beam frame, foundation, roof and tower are pegged and bolted together and secured with 1 1/2-inch thick iron rods. The building was ornamented with the mansard roof and scrolled window frames typical of the then-fashionable French Second Empire style.

The Lighthouse served as both the home and workplace for eleven successive keepers and their families. The first floor was divided into a living room and kitchen, the second into four bedrooms. Heat was provided by coal stoves, and water was pumped from the lake. Both bell and beacon were used to guide navigators. In 1933, the Lighthouse was decommissioned when the hand-operated system was replaced by an automatic electric beacon, making the manned facility obsolete.

In 1952, Vermont historian Ralph Nading Hill ferried Electra Havemeyer Webb out to the reef to explore the now-derelict building. Entranced, she decided to move the lighthouse to the Museum. Undaunted by the hazards involved, her veteran crew of carpenters moved heavy beams, stairways, doors and windows through rough lake waters to the mainland and re-erected it on the Museum site.

Exhibits in the Lighthouse illustrate Lake Champlain navigation, military history, commercial traffic and life in a lighthouse.

The Meeting House, which measures 36 by 48 feet, was built in 1840 in Charlotte, Vermont, by the Methodist congregation. Its triangular pediment, created by cornice moldings, is a reflection of the Greek Revival style, and the lack of other adornment is typical of New England protestant architecture.

By 1899, the meeting house had ceased to function as a church and was taken over as a playhouse by thirteen young women who formed an amateur theatrical group. In 1902, the group incorporated as the Breezy Point Library Association and bought the building to serve as the town library. A heavy windstorm damaged the building in 1950, and the association voted to sell it to the Museum so it could be preserved.

In 1952, the building was dismantled and moved to the Museum grounds. Replacements for missing or damaged elements, including the belfrey, pews and pulpit, were salvaged from an abandoned church in Milton, Vermont. The interior plaster walls  were painted in tones of white and grey to resemble paneled woodwork.

Today, the Meeting House serves as a reminder of the role of such gathering places in the religious, social and civic lives of Vermonters. As an element of the Museum's campus, it continues to function as the site for performances, lectures and meetings.

The Pleissner Gallery was constructed at the Museum in 1986 as a memorial to Brooklyn-born artist Ogden Minton Pleissner (1905-1983), a close friend of the Webb family who earned national recognition for his watercolors and oil renderings of landscapes and sporting scenes. The main gallery contains a selection of his work; the adjoining room is a recreation of his Manchester, Vermont, studio, complete with canvases, brushes and personal memorabilia.

Pleissner received his formal training at the Art Students League in New York City. During the 1930s he spent summers in Wyoming, building a reputation as an accomplished painter of Western landscapes. Pleissner served as a war artist for the U.S. Air Force and *Life Magazine* during WWII, completing many watercolors in war torn France and England. In later years he painted in Europe, Nova Scotia, New York City (where he maintained a winter studio) and Vermont. Pleissner was the recipient of many honors and awards, including a gold medal from the American Watercolor Society.

Prentis House

The Prentis House, built in Hadley, Massachusetts, in 1773 by the Dickenson family, was moved to its present site in 1955. It is typical of New England "saltbox" architecture, so-called because the asymetrical roof line resembles the profile of early wooden salt containers. The front of the house is two stories high, with a gable roof that extends down over the low rear of the house. The Prentis House is built around a massive central chimney, which supports much of the building's weight. Seven flues meet on the second floor in a huge beehive-shaped formation before the chimney narrows again at the roofline.

Katherine Prentis Murphy, a well-known antique collector who had created furnished period rooms at the New Hampshire and New-York Historical Societies, became acquainted with Electra Havemeyer Webb through a circle of collectors interested in American antiques and decorative arts. Katherine Murphy took a keen interest in Electra Webb's growing museum and offered to furnish a house. Electra Webb's scouts found the abandoned Dickenson house while seeking a source for wall paneling and floorboards. The age of the house and its floor plan seemed to Electra Webb to make it the perfect setting for Katherine Prentis Murphy's proposed gift of 17th- and 18th-century decorative arts. Together, they acquired and placed examples of William and Mary furniture and English delftware ceramics, stumpwork embroideries, flame-stitched upholstery and curtains, and Oriental carpets in the parlor and dining room. Resist-dyed, crewel-embroidered and quilted bedclothes are featured in the second-story chambers. Electra Webb named the newly furnished house for her friend and colleague.

The "period room" designers of the 1950s created an attractive, though historically flawed, picture of the colonial interior; subsequent scholars working with household inventories and other documents have discovered that early American life was more austere than the first period rooms indicated. In recent years, many museums have dismantled such exhibits. Shelburne continues to preserve the Prentis House as an example of the early efforts of collectors and museums to recreate the colonial household.

The Ben Lane Printing Shop was constructed on the Museum grounds in 1955 using historic timbers and has held several exhibits. Today the building accommodates a typical, small-town printing shop of the first half of the 20th century.

Although the modern process of offset lithography was used in the larger printing businesses of this same period, rural shops were slow to adapt to the new technology. A shop like this Museum's with moveable metal type continued to use time-honored methods of letterpress production in a system similar to that devised by Johann Gutenberg in the mid 1400s.

The exhibit in the Ben Lane Printing Shop represents equipment that might have been accumulated by a proprietor and his successors as they struggled to keep up with technological improvements over a half century or more of operation. In the first decades of the 20th century, presses of many eras continued to be used for specific purposes. Even a 1820s vintage handpress would remain in occasional service. The Cotrell newspaper press, manufactured in 1871, would roll on a regular basis, as would a treadle-operated Dorman job press of the same vintage for smaller work. Although racks of wood and metal type would still be in use, a complicated and often cantankerous Linotype machine would fulfill many of the shop's composition requirements. Finally, the latest addition, a high-speed Heidelberg press with automatic inking and paper feed, would operate quickly and efficiently, dramatically increasing the output of work.

The Museum's printing shop was named in honor of Benjamin Battles Lane (1897-1987) whose father, Frank, founded the Lane Press of Burlington in 1900. Ben Lane served as president and general manager of Lane Press from 1928-1961. His support enabled the Museum to install this exhibit and open it to the general public as a living tribute to a centuries-old craft.

Shelburne Museum operates the Ben Lane Printing Shop as a working exhibit. A variety of presses and other equipment are demonstrated to visitors on a daily basis. The shop is also the site of educational programs for children and adults and manufactures retail items for the Museum stores.

Rail Car *Grand Isle*

The Rail Car *Grand Isle* was built by the Wagner Palace Car Company about 1890 and presented by the company's president, Dr. William Seward Webb, to Vermont Governor Edward C. Smith. The car's mahogany-paneled parlor, elegant

dining room, staterooms and plush furnishings are typical of the private luxury cars that became important symbols of rank to railroad men, business tycoons and public figures of the final quarter of the 19th century.

Dr. Webb, educated as a physician, was persuaded by his father-in-law, William Henry Vanderbilt, to give up the medical profession and join the family's network of railroad enterprises. As president of the Rutland Railroad and the Wagner Palace Car Company, Webb lived for part of the year in Shelburne, Vermont, commuting to business in New York City with relative ease. His own private car, the *Ellsmere*, was similar to the Museum's *Grand Isle*.

When purchased for the Museum in 1960, the *Grand Isle* had been converted for business use, its paneling painted, fixtures replaced and plush furnishings removed. J. Watson Webb, Jr., Dr. Webb's grandson, supervised the car's renovation to evoke the grand days of luxury rail travel and commemorate his family's role in the railroad industry.

The Rail Locomotive No. 220, built in 1915 by the American Locomotive Company of Schenectady, New York, was the last coal-burning, steam ten-wheeler used on the Central Vermont Railway. As a medium-sized 4-6-0 engine (4 leading wheels, 6 driving wheels, and 0 trailing small wheels), it served double duty in Vermont pulling both freight and passenger trains. No. 220 became known as "The Locomotive of the Presidents" because of its use on special trains carrying Calvin Coolidge, Herbert Hoover, Franklin D. Roosevelt and Dwight D. Eisenhower.

Steam locomotives were the only type of engine in the United States until 1895, when the first electric train was introduced; they continued to dominate until the 1950s when the diesel engine gained wide acceptance. The inscription "28%" on the coal tender means that the engine could lift or drag approximately twenty-eight thousand pounds of dead weight. The Central Vermont Railway retired No. 220 from service in 1956 and presented it to the Museum for preservation. The shed was built soon afterward to protect the locomotive and the private car from the elements.

Railroad Station and Freight Shed

The Shelburne Railroad Station, built in 1890 by Rutland Railroad President Dr. William Seward Webb, was originally located near the center of Shelburne to conveniently serve passengers of the Central Vermont and Rutland Railroads. The building was designed by Robert Henderson Robertson, architect of the Shelburne Farms' house and barns, and is stylistically consistent with the Webb estate. Robertson chose freely from the late 19th-century architectural vocabulary, combining strongly overhanging eaves supported by brackets, with hipped and curved roofs, flared walls and eyebrow windows.

Passenger service to the community was discontinued in 1953. Dr. Webb's son Vanderbilt Webb and son-in-law Cyril Jones gave the station to the Museum and it was moved to its present site in 1959. Waiting rooms for men and women and the stationmaster's office were restored. Telegraphy systems, railroad memorabilia and maps help to complete a picture of late 19th- and early 20th-century rail travel.

In addition to the main depot, every railroad maintained a variety of outbuildings for storage. The small annex to the Shelburne Station was built by the Museum to exhibit hand tools and equipment used by railroad workers and includes handcarts, picks and shovels, and signal lanterns from railroad lines around the country. Also on exhibit is the *Gertie Buck*, a small homemade, steam-driven car formerly used to carry passengers on the Woodstock (Vermont) Railroad.

The Round Barn, a three-story building measuring eighty feet in diameter, was constructed in 1901 by Fred "Silo" Quimby in East Passumpsic, Vermont. Round barns enjoyed a brief period of popularity in the late 19th and early 20th centuries. The first round barn in America was built by the Shakers in 1826, at Hancock, Massachusetts. The design was reintroduced in 1896 and building plans published in a nationally distributed farm journal sparked the construction of approximately twenty-four such barns in Vermont beginning in 1899.

Economy of labor was the fundamental aim of round barn design. Hay, stored in the spacious top floor, and silage, stored in the central silo, could be easily dropped through feed chutes to the level below. There up to sixty cows could be stanchioned around the center for feeding and milking. Manure was shoveled through trap doors to the basement where it could be col-

lected by horse-drawn wagons.

The Round Barn was moved from Passumpsic to Shelburne in 1985 and 1986. The upper segment of the silo, weighing nine thousand pounds, was carried to the site by helicopter, while the remainder was dismantled piece by piece and moved on flatbed trucks. New materials were required to replace what had aged beyond use.

The uppermost level of the Barn is now used as the Museum's visitor orientation center. Agricultural exhibits and museum slide presentations and videos are located on the lower levels.

Sawmill

The Sawmill building was constructed at the Museum in l957 to house equipment originally used in the Trescott-Shepard sawmill in South Royalton, Vermont. The equipment, dating from 1787, includes an up-and-down saw, extra saw blades and logging tools. Historically, the term "sawmill" was used to refer to either the mill building or the machinery it contained. The original South Royalton mill was built on Mill Brook by Jeremiah Trescott and his partner, Captain Stevens, in the late 1700s.

The Shepard family, descendants of Trescott, continued operating the mill until the early 20th century and later donated it to the Shelburne Museum. The water wheel, deteriorated through use over the years, was replaced with a historically accurate reproduction in l990.

The Museum's sawmill illustrates the principle by which the force of moving water powers moveable machine parts to create useful energy. When the mill was in operation, the water power enabled a saw blade to move up and down and cut through a log directed into its path. At full speed, the saw cut two strokes per second, allowing the sawyer to cut a ten-foot board in eight minutes. Slowly but effectively, boards were sliced from even the stoutest of logs.

In early America wood was needed to construct everything from sailing ships to buckets and storage kegs. Very quickly lumber emerged as the most important cash crop of 18th-century America. Villages grew and prospered when associated with a major waterway and the sawmills, gristmills and textile mills that it powered.

The Sawyer's Cabin is a one-room house built in East Charlotte, Vermont, about 1800. It is constructed of hand-hewn beech and pine timbers, dovetailed at the corners; the ceiling and floor joists are dovetailed into the outside walls.

Log cabins were often built by Vermont settlers, loggers and trappers as temporary homes. This example is thought to have been built by French Canadians who were lumbering in East Charlotte. Several similar cabins have been found in the vicinity.

When acquired by the Museum in 1955, the log structure was faced with clapboards that had protected the log substructure. The building was moved to the Museum intact, restored, and furnished

as a historic house. The interior is a single room with a stone fireplace. A loft reached by ladder might have provided additional sleeping space. Its simple rustic furniture, household implements and textiles suggest the hardships of life in rural 19th-century Vermont. French Canadian furniture, including a cupboard, a bench, chairs and children's beds are among the furnishings.

Schoolhouse

The Schoolhouse was built about 1840 in Vergennes, Vermont. Moderate classical influences are apparent in its projecting bell tower, arched door opening and sash windows. The surface pattern of the exterior walls was achieved by the bricklayer, who alternated six rows of stretchers (horizontally-laid bricks) with one row of headers (end-laid bricks) to form subtle bands that circle the building. The one-room interior measures thirty feet by twenty-two feet.

The building originally stood on land leased to Vergennes by General Samuel Strong, a Revolutionary War officer and descendant of one of Addison County's first families. Strong had stipulated that the schoolhouse property  be used for educational purposes at the annual rent of one kernel of Indian corn, payable to him on the first of January.

By the mid 1940s the structure had been abandoned for many years and was in need of restoration. The brick schoolhouse was relocated to its present site in 1947. Careful drawings were created before the belfry was removed and the brickwork dismantled piece by piece. The tinwork of the original dome was replaced with copper, its surmounting acorn finial repaired, missing windows replaced, plaster walls resurfaced, and bell rehung. Desks, benches, maps, and examples of children's schoolwork were assembled to furnish the 19th-century rural school.

The Shaker Shed, an unornamented commercial structure, originally served a large Shaker community in Canterbury, New Hampshire. Built in 1840 as a one-story horse and carriage stand, the heavy timber framework is strengthened by five granite pillars visible between carriage bays. The basic structure was enlarged twice over a period of thirteen years. In 1850, one and a half upper stories were added to provide storage space for brooms made and sold by community members. In 1853, a farm machinery shed was added to the rear.

Dubbed "Shakers" because of the frenetic dancing involved in their worship service, the religious sect to which the Canterbury community belonged was formally known as the United Society of Believers in the First and Second Appearance of Christ. Self-sufficiency, hard work, and celibacy were its guiding principles. The Shakers were widely known in the 19th century for the quality of their crafts and garden products. Un-adorned and finely

crafted furnishings, seeds and herbal medicines were first produced for community use and later sold nationwide by wagon and by mail.

The Shaker Shed was moved to the Museum in 1951 to serve as exhibition space for collections of handtools and household equipment. A vast array of woodworking tools, supplemented by groups of cobbler and harnessmaker tools and household implements, is exhibited in upper stories of the shed; firefighting equipment is shown in the former horse stand.

Smokehouse

The Smokehouse, built in Charlotte, Vermont, around 1820, is a small stone structure with a dirt floor. The major structural requirement of a smokehouse was that the building be airtight, although chimneys and small vents were sometimes installed to regulate the density of smoke.

It was within this confined chamber that meat was treated to prevent spoilage. Traditionally, butchered cuts were soaked in brine, then hung in a smokehouse above a smoldering fire of corn cobs and hickory wood. Meats remained in place for several days, or sometimes weeks, to complete the process. The distinctive flavor acquired in the process was an additional benefit. Smokehouses similar to the Shelburne Museum Smokehouse were used on farms throughout America until the late 19th century.

The Stagecoach Inn was built in Charlotte, Vermont, in 1783. The regularly spaced windows flanking a central door with sidelights reflect the Georgian building style popular in 18th-century America. The Inn's builder was Hezakiah Barnes, a former captain in the United States Militia, who moved with his family to Charlotte from Lanesboro, Massachusetts. Barnes, a road surveyor, placed his inn and a trading post on opposite sides of the main stage route from Montreal to points south.

When the building was dismantled and reassembled on the Museum grounds in 1949, it needed restoration. The second-story ballroom, which had been divided into bedrooms, was returned to its former dimensions. Ten fireplaces housing two brick ovens and two ham-smoking chambers were rebuilt. Paneling and plaster finishes approximating those found in New England in the late 18th century were applied. Replacement window casings and chair rails were fashioned with antique carpenter's planes. A broad porch, built onto the original building but absent in 1949, was rebuilt to recreate the Inn's early appearance.

Today the Inn serves as a setting for sculptural pieces from Shelburne's folk art collection. Tobacconists' figures, trade signs, ship figureheads and patriotic carvings are among the pieces on view.

The Stencil House, originally built in Columbus, New York, is a typical example of the type of small side-gabled house built throughout New York and New England in the 17th and 18th centuries. The floor plan groups four rooms around a central chimney. The centrally located front door, flanked by pairs of double-hung windows, opens into a small entrance hall. Historic maps and deeds indicate that the house was built about 1804 on a farm lot of approximately one hundred acres.

The Museum acquired the building in 1953 because of the paint-decorated walls that could be seen through gaps in the wallpaper. Before moving the house to Shelburne, several layers of peeling paper were removed, revealing the scope of the painted decoration. Rather than confining motifs to borders, the Stencil House artist had covered entire walls of the entrance hall, parlor and dining room, working directly on boards rather than on plaster walls. This work was probably completed sometime between 1810 and 1830.

The parlor and dining room contain groupings of paint-decorated and unpainted vernacular furniture and accessories, aesthetically compatible with the stenciled designs. An 1870 photograph of the farm and another of its owners were given to the Museum by descendents of the family. The house is dedicated to John Kenneth Byard, a colleague and friend of Electra Havemeyer Webb who helped to select many of the furnishings.

The Stone Cottage was built about 1840 in South Burlington, Vermont, as a dairy laborer's house. The first tenants were a family of five that included two children and an elderly parent. In later years the building served as a school and a blacksmith shop. The house is constructed of limestone laid in straight courses rather than in the more common scatterstone technique.

Only the outside walls remained when the cottage was acquired by the Museum in 1947. In 1949, the stones were individually numbered before being moved piece by piece to the Museum where they were reassembled. By

luck a direct descendant of the original owner of the building heard about the project. Her recollections of the interior as it had looked eighty years before enabled Museum staff to duplicate the floor plan. She remembered much about the family who had lived in the house and gave the Museum the original wrought-iron door latch that she had removed years before when the building began to slip into ruin. Restoration of the cottage incorporated old beams and materials from local barns, homes and other buildings that had been abandoned.

The furniture, textiles and household goods exhibited in the Stone Cottage illustrate the simple lifestyle of agricultural workers in the mid-19th century.

Ticonderoga

The steamboat *Ticonderoga* is America's last remaining side paddlewheel passenger steamer with a vertical beam engine of the type that provided freight and passenger service on America's lakes and rivers from the early 19th to mid-20th centuries. Commissioned by the Champlain Transportation Company, the *Ticonderoga* was built in 1906 at the Shelburne Shipyard on Lake Champlain.

The *Ti* measures 220 feet in length and 59 feet in beam, with a displacement of 892 tons. Her steam-powered engine, handmade by the Fletcher Engine Company of Hoboken, New Jersey, was powered by two coal-fired boilers and could achieve a maximum speed of seventeen miles per hour. Her full crew numbered twenty-eight, and included the captain, pilots, mate, deckhands, engineers and firemen to operate the boat. The purser, stewardess, freight clerk, bartender, hall boys, cook, waiters, scullion and mess boys attended to passenger and freight arrangements.

Initially, the *Ticonderoga* served a north-south route on Lake Champlain. Daily, she docked at

Westport, New York, where she met the New York City evening train. The next morning she carried travelers and freight northward to St. Albans, Vermont. In addition to passengers, the *Ti* transported local farm produce, livestock and dry goods on a regular basis, and during both World Wars ferried U.S. troops between Plattsburgh, New York, and Burlington, Vermont. Over the years she also operated on the east-west run from Burlington to Port Kent, New York, and had a brief career as a floating casino.

When more modern ferries made her obsolete, the *Ti* was operated as an excursion boat by new owners for several seasons, but by 1950 a steady decline in business threatened the boat's future. The *Ti* was saved from the scrap heap by Ralph Nading Hill, a devoted Vermont historian, who persuaded Electra Havemeyer Webb to buy her. The Museum kept her in operation, but the steamboat era had passed, making it difficult to find qualified personnel to operate and maintain the aging vessel.

In 1954, the decision was made to move the *Ti* overland to the Museum. At the end of the summer season, the boat sailed into a newly dug, water-filled basin off Shelburne Bay and floated over a railroad carriage resting on specially laid tracks. The water was then pumped out of the basin, and the *Ti* settled

onto the railroad carriage. During the winter of 1955, the *Ti* was hauled across highways, over a swamp, through woods and fields and across the tracks of the Rutland Railroad to reach her permanent mooring on the Museum grounds.

Much of the boat's interior has been restored to its original grandeur. The dining room and stateroom halls are paneled in butternut and cherry; ceilings are stencilled in gold. The barber shop, Captain's quarters, dining room and promenade deck contain furniture and accessories used on the *Ticonderoga* and other Lake Champlain steamboats. The *Ti* was declared a National Historic Landmark in 1960.

Toy Shop

The Toy Shop adjoins the Museum's Variety Unit, which was built around 1835 and remains on its original site. The Variety Unit is typical of the "continuous architecture" farmhouses that are still seen throughout Vermont; carrying forth that tradition, the Toy Shop was added by the Museum to house a collection of children's playthings.

Dolls, dollhouses and toys were among the first collections Electra Havemeyer Webb installed in the Variety Unit; the collection of toys grew so large that by the early 1950s, the separate Toy Shop exhibition

was created to show the range of playthings available during the 19th and early 20th centuries.

The Museum's toy collection includes many items that mirror their full-scale counterparts elsewhere on the grounds. Miniature transportation toys include firewagons, steamboats, trains and a locomotive; dolls attending a tea party dine from miniature ceramics resembling those displayed in period rooms. The penny banks, music boxes and Noah's Ark of an earlier era make an interesting contrast to the tiny cars and motorcycles of a more recent period.

The Variety Unit, a brick farmhouse built about 1835 in Shelburne, Vermont, is the only historic structure at the Museum original to the site. It is a rambling building with a complex interior created by a series of one- and two-room additions in the New England tradition of "continuous architecture." Although the current entrance is located at the west end of the building, the original front facade with its Greek Revival features, including front-gable orientation and a fully articulated pediment, is on the east side of the house.

Originally known as the Weed House, the building was renamed the Variety Unit for the wide range of decorative arts exhibited there. The first room in the building recreates the dining room of the Webb family home in Westbury, Long Island. This setting demonstrates the manner in which Electra Havemeyer Webb incorporated American antiques into her home long before the Museum was founded.

The remainder of the Variety Unit is a series of galleries in which individual collections are exhibited: English ceramics ranging from Whieldon and Staffordshire to Toby jugs and mochaware, Chinese export porcelain, American and European pewter, clocks, blown and pressed glass, and scrimshaw. The gallery devoted to Commodore Thomas Macdonough, hero of the War of 1812, provides a context for the transfer-printed china decorated with scenes of his victory on Lake Champlain. The second-floor galleries exhibit Mrs. Webb's collections of dolls, dollhouses, miniature furniture and music boxes.

The Vermont House was until 1929 the home of descendants of Asa R. Slocumb, who arrived in Shelburne in 1790. His first home was a log cabin. According to legend, he built the present house around and over his log cabin, and when the house was completed, he dismantled the cabin and carried away the logs.

When the Slocumb house came to the Museum in 1950, the clapboards and interior walls had so deteriorated that beyond the basic structure little could be salvaged. Stone from a Shelburne Falls gristmill, laid in the random scatterstone technique, formed replacement facades, while the feather-edged boards of the interior walls came from Vermont and New Hampshire houses. The paneling on the fireplace wall in the parlor came from the Essex, Connecticut, region. Although the four fireplaces are original to the building, the floor plan was altered to include a study and a larger kitchen.

Museum founder Electra Havemeyer Webb envisioned the Vermont House to be the setting for an imaginary retired sea captain of some wealth who had gathered his possessions over the decades of his travels, and built himself a fine house in which to place them. As such, it exhibits high style American furnishings of the Queen Anne and Chippendale periods combined with French and English decorative accessories. Particularly notable are a block-front chest of drawers, an elaborately pedimented desk and secretary, and handpainted maritime wallpaper.

The building which serves as the Museum's Weaving Shop was constructed on the site in 1955 using salvaged building materials. It offers on-going demonstrations of spinning and weaving, and exhibits a variety of historic textiles, including blankets, coverlets, towels, tablecoths and yardage used for curtains and clothing.

Craftspeople demonstrate the range of traditional skills utilized in processing raw wool and flax into woven cloth. Fibers are prepared for spinning using a combination of hand tools, among them flax hetchels and wool combs to align fibers. Spinning wheels, both the large walking wheel and smaller flax wheels, are employed to spin the wool or flax fibers into twisted strands. Yarn winders ply strands together to form strengthened threads and yarns.

Weaving is demonstrated on historic looms. Barn frame looms, dating from the late 18th and early 19th centuries, were used to produce everything from yardage for clothing to bedding, carpets and sacks. Before the weaving trade was industrialized, the work was done either at home or, more frequently, in small shops.

The Shelburne Museum weavers use barn frame looms to produce placemats, table runners, small rugs and yardage. An 1890's Jacquard loom, restored over a two year period in the early 1980s, is used to weave elaborate floral and mosaic patterns. Noted not only for its ability to produce such patterns, the Jacquard loom remains today an important example of early "automated" looms of the type that, when combined with a power source, eventually made mass-produced textiles possible.

The Webb Gallery was constructed in 1960 to blend with neighboring historic structures. With a main block flanked by matched wings, its design echoes the symmetry and scale of the nearby Dorset House; bricks, chosen as the primary exterior material, reflect the texture and color of the Schoolhouse and Meeting House. Behind the old-fashioned facade, however, is a modern truss-roofed structure with technological systems that provide the proper environment for the preservation of artwork.

American paintings, decorative arts and works on paper are exhibited in the Webb Gallery. These include a collection of 19th-century portraits, landscapes and genre scenes by such artists as William Matthew Prior, Erastus Salisbury Field, Winslow Homer, and Fitz Hugh Lane.

Twentieth-century painters Anna Mary Robertson Moses (known also as Grandma Moses) and Andrew Wyeth are also on view. The lower-level galleries present paintings of Vermont subjects or by Vermont artists as well as changing exhibitions of prints from the Museum's permanent collections.

"Stock Farm and Res. of Wm. Powers, Town of Leicester, Addison Co. Vt," *Combination Atlas of Vermont 1876.* H.W. Burgett & Co., engraved and printed by Beers. (1989-52)

Spade plow, c. 1780-1820. Maker unknown, Vermont. Wood. (2.6.1-3)

"American Type" Bee Hive, 1880s. "Man'f'd by/W. O. Sweet," W. Mansfield, Mass. Wood, painted white with green stenciled decoration. Gift of E. J. Cope. (2.5.9-18)

AGRICULTURAL IMPLEMENTS

Shelburne Museum's collection of agriculture-related artifacts reflects the rural nature of Vermont and New England. The Round Barn exhibition "Living Off the Land" interprets and illustrates the history of Vermont farming with hand- and animal-powered tools, advertising broadsides, tool catalogues and farm journals associated with different farm chores.

Most early Vermont farmers maintained small diversified farms on rugged terrain with a team of oxen, a few cows, sheep, chickens, and pigs. They raised enough crops to feed their families and livestock, and to provide extra goods to sell or barter. In the winter they cared for their livestock, harvested ice for refrigeration and logged for firewood, fence posts and lumber. As the days grew warmer, they gathered sap to produce maple syrup and sugar. The spring heralded planting, the summer growing, and the fall harvest. The entire family participated in seasonal chores.

In the early 19th century the introduction of new breeds of sheep, dairy cows, cattle, horses, swine and poultry encouraged farmers to expand their operations. The development of New England's textile industry created a demand for good quality, long-staple wool for weaving cloth and blankets. Vermont sheep farmers began focusing their efforts on specialty breeds, and by 1840, Vermont was famous around the world for its Merino sheep and wool production.

By the mid 1800s, however, Vermont farmers began turning to dairy products. Sheep farming had declined because of western competition, and dairy cows could yield as much as 70% more at market than sheep. A large market for butter, cheese and milk had developed in southern New England and New York cities. By 1880, Vermonters led the country in the production of milk, cheese and butter and the state census recorded more cows than people.

Also in the late 1800s, Vermont beekeepers enjoyed a national reputation both for the quality of their honey and for the numerous inventions of hives, honey extractors, swarm catchers and other beekeeping equipment. Continual improvements and new inventions of tools and machines for clearing and plowing fields, planting, cultivating and harvesting crops enabled farmers to increase their production.

C.Y.O.

Exhibited in: Dutton House, Round Barn, Shaker Shed, Webb Gallery

Agricultural Implements

Beaded and quillwork moccasins, late 19th century. Makers unknown, Plains Indians. Leather with glass and dyed porcupine quill decoration. Gift of Ogden Pleissner.

Water vessel, late 19th century. Maker unknown, Pueblo Indian. Earthenware with white and black slip decoration. (46.9-6)

Chilkat blanket, late 19th century. Maker unknown, Tlingit, Northwest coast of North America. Woven mountain goat and mountain sheep wools, analine dyes, cedar bark and wool cloth. (46.11-5)

Long before contact with European explorers, people native to the Americas had developed many distinct cultural and aesthetic traditions and languages. Guided by their traditions, the craftspeople of these different nations created utilitarian household goods such as baskets, ceramics, clothing and storage containers of wood and bark, as well as ceremonial or sacred objects including masks, rattles, drums and dance costumes.

When newcomers from Europe and Africa arrived in the Western Hemisphere, America's native people incorporated newly available materials into their craft traditions, both adapting products for their own use and creating new ones suitable for the changed market.

Shelburne's collection of American Indian artifacts was acquired by travelers in the early decades of the 20th century. Although by this time many Indian people were producing handcrafted objects for the tourist market, pieces with traditional significance were available as well. To many collectors, American Indian objects represented an aesthetic style that was uniquely American and cultures that were closely linked with the unspoiled American landscape. Objects in the collection were chosen for their beauty and interest, and include pieces from cultures across North America.

The Chilkat blanket from southern Alaska exhibited in the Beach Lodge, for example, was made for personal use: its design and the right to wear it in ceremonial dances were hereditary property of the owner's family. In contrast, the totem poles, panel and mask that now decorate the Beach Lodge were carved and painted in the early decades of the 20th century by skilled traditional woodworkers of the Northwest Coast who created them for sale rather than ceremonial use.

The decoration of objects with beadwork for personal and family use became a highly developed art form in the mid- to late 19th century. The beaded moccasins, gauntlets, leggings and saddlebags exhibited in the Beach Gallery were made by people of the Sioux, Cheyenne and other Plains nations in a style that developed after about 1840, when tiny glass "seed" beads were substituted for the traditional dyed porcupine quills. Among the costume accessories exhibited in the Hat and Fragrance Textile Gallery are purses with intricate floral beadwork patterns created by Iroquois craftspeople of this era. Workmanship eventually declined in much of the beadwork made for sale. Tourists unfamiliar with traditional standards of design and production often

American Indian Artifacts

Parfleche, c. 1900-1920. Maker unknown, Plains Indian. Painted rawhide. Gift of Ogden Pleissner. (46.2-3)

Basket, late 19th century. Maker unknown, Salish, Pacific Northwest. Cedar and grass. (46.10-00)

Man's shirt, late 19th century. Maker unknown, Plains Indian. Elkhide beads, fur. Gift of Ogden M. Pleissner. (46.1-30)

AMERICAN INDIAN ARTIFACTS

were unwilling to pay the price for the most labor-intensive pieces.

In the southwestern United States, however, the interest of tourists provided an economic incentive that led to the revival of finely crafted ceramics. Artists of the Zuni, Acoma and Hopi not only maintained their distinctive forms and motifs, but began early in the 20th century to rediscover the methods used by their ancestors to create magnificent pottery bowls and storage vessels in prehistoric times. Examples of southwestern pottery may be seen in the Beach Lodge.

Like many other collections at the Shelburne Museum, the American Indian artifacts exhibited here are examples of utilitarian objects enhanced by traditional methods of decoration—methods and traditions, moreover, that were in danger of disappearing at the time when the objects were acquired. In addition to the exhibits in the Beach Gallery and Lodge, pieces of American Indian origin can be found exhibited with the Museum's collections of baskets, costume accessories and dolls.
E.B.

Exhibited in: Beach Lodge and Gallery, Hat and Fragrance Textile Gallery, Variety Unit

Shaker-style gathering basket, date unknown. Maker unknown. Wood. (35.11-139)

Eel trap, date unknown. Maker unknown. Wood, metal, cork and hemp. (35.11-83)

Market basket, late 19th century. Cemore Landon Morehouse, Vermont. Wood and metal. (35.11-74)

Basketmaking is one of the earliest crafts, pre-dating both pottery and weaving. Practiced by cultures the world over and in North America as early as 6,000 B.C., the interlacing of native plant fibers resulted in a huge variety of storage and carrying vessels, simple furniture, hunting and fishing implements, and even watercraft and stock fences.

Baskets played an integral role in early America, serving primarily the farm, home and small business to transport goods, gather produce, and store food and other items. Most basketmakers worked fulltime at some other occupation and plied their basketmaking skill in the winter when the weather limited other activities; those who were highly skilled sold and bartered their work. Technique and style developed over time. Traditional New England basketry reflects the melding of cultural backgrounds as immigrants from European countries adapted their skills to indigenous plants and the techniques practiced by American Indians for centuries.

It was not until the mid-19th century with the advent of water power and attendant mechanization that the preparation of raw materials allowed for commercial manufacture of baskets. Formerly ash and oak splints were prepared entirely by hand, requiring "basket logs" to be beaten with a wooden or metal-headed mallet. This applied pressure would dislodge fibers between growth rings, allowing the basketmaker to pull strips of veneer from the log. These rough strips—called splints—would then need to be cut to size. Further preparations might include additional splitting to refine the thickness, or scraping to create a smooth, uniform surface. Now the bulk of this time-consuming and arduous work—beating the logs—could be accomplished by machines.

The Museum's collection of nearly two hundred baskets includes a wide range of forms, styles, materials and techniques. The basket exhibit in the Shaker Shed provides a good overview. Among the many types represented are those using a simple over-and-under weave, including an oak splint eel trap, an ash splint pigeon basket used to carry birds to market, a Vermont basket with a mass-produced wire swing handle, and a paint-decorated buckboard storage basket. Coiled basketry technique is demonstrated by a rye grass serving basket; ribbed basket construction by an oak market basket; hexagonal weave by a cheese basket; and Shaker technique—noted for its tight weave, wrapped rim binding and carved handles—by oak splint gathering baskets.

Cheese basket, c. 1850-1900. Maker unknown. Hexagonal weave, ash. (35.11-13)

Poultry cage, 20th century. John T. Ronco, Maine. Wood splint, seagrass and wire. (35.11-80)

(Left to right) Rib-style gathering basket, gathering basket with swing handle, and gathering basket, dates and makers unknown. Wood. (35.11-28, 35.11-49, 35.11-47)

Additional baskets made for specialized agricultural tasks are on exhibit in the Round Barn, Dutton House and General Store. These include a willow winnowing basket, berry baskets and a straw bee hive.

The Museum's collections also include a variety of examples of American Indian baskets dating from the mid- to late l9th century, many of which may have been made for the emerging tourist trade. Coiled storage baskets made by Hopi Indians are on display in the Beach Lodge, as are twined cedar baskets, many with overlaid fiber designs, made by Northwest Coast Indians.

By the mid-l9th century, northeastern basketmakers of American Indian and European background had developed a shared regional style of ash splint baskets made in a wide variety of forms, some decorated with stamped vegetable dye patterns. Certain stamped patterns, decorative overlaid splint weaves, and the construction of plaited sweet grass baskets emerged as the hallmarks of American Indian craftspeople. Examples of these may be located in both the Shaker Shed and General Store exhibits. *C.W.*

Exhibited in: Beach Lodge, Dutton House, General Store, Round Barn, Shaker Shed

The Last Drop, 1903. Charles
Schreyvogel. Bronze. Gift of Kate
Webb Harris, Laura Webb Brown
and Dundeen Webb Galipeau.
(26-49)

*Petite
danseuse de
quatorze ans*,
1922. Edgar
Degas. Bronze
cast from
original wax.
(26-16)

*Indian Mounted on
Elephant Crushing
a Tiger*, after
1848. Antoine-
Louis Barye.
Bronze. (26-4)

Sculptors have been casting their ideas in bronze since around 2300 B.C. The Romans perfected the process and by the early 1500s monumental bronze statues of heroes on horseback, saints and monarchs stood in public squares all over Europe, while smaller figures decorated churches and the homes of art patrons. Bronze sculpture is made by using a mold or by casting from an original model. Either process allows an artist to create several nearly identical copies of one work of art. In the 19th century, technological changes improved the production of multiple casts and smaller, table-top sculptures became fashionable and affordable. Both European and American art collectors decorated their parlors with statues of animals, classical goddesses and romantic figures.

Shelburne's bronze collection focuses on these small, decorative bronzes. Bronze castings of exotic animals by French artist Antoine Louis Barye may be seen in the Electra Havemeyer Wcbb Memorial Building. His small sculptures of elephants, crocodiles and lions are displayed in the library. Barye spent hours at the Paris Zoo sketching the anatomy of animals to accurately reproduce them in bronze. His sculpture *Elephant and Driver,* located in the foyer, captures the rough skin of an elephant and the contrasting soft cloth costume of his driver.

A bronze casting of Edgar Degas' famous *Petite danseuse de quatorze ans* is also exhibited in the foyer. The original sculpture was modeled in wax and dressed in a gauze skirt, silk chemise and horsehair wig. The exhibition of the wax figure in 1881 caused a sensation. Some critics praised Degas as innovative while others condemned him for not using a more elegant medium like marble. It was not until after the artist's death in 1917 that the wax dancer was cast into bronze in an edition of twenty-two. Other Degas bronzes of horses and riders, also originally modeled in wax, may be seen in the living room. Degas studied horses and jockeys as a way to explore the effects of form, space and motion.

The Beach Gallery houses a collection of 19th- and 20th-century American bronzes featuring work by such Western artists as Charles Russell and Harry Jackson. These artists, who often served as cowhands and guides on the Western Plains, modeled their work after real people or personal experiences. Their bucking broncos and portraits of Native Americans and cowboys are romantic interpretations of a vanishing American West.
L.B.H.

Exhibited in: Beach Gallery, Bostwick Garden, Electra Havemeyer Webb Memorial Building

Bronze Sculpture

Peacock, c. 1900. Maker unknown, possibly German. Carved and painted wood. (FC 12)

Giraffe, c. 1895. Gustav A. Dentzel Carousel Company, Philadelphia, Penn. Carved and painted wood with glass, leather, brass and iron attachments. (FC 7-12)

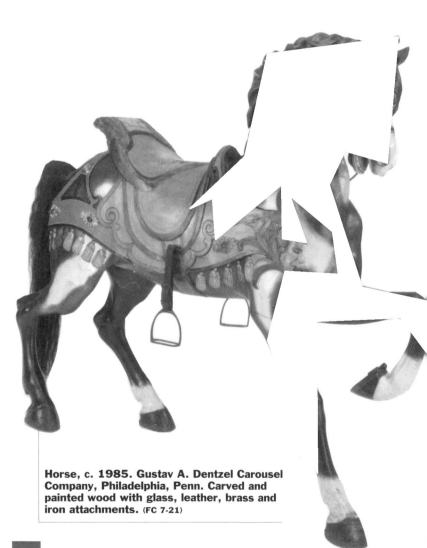

Horse, c. 1985. Gustav A. Dentzel Carousel Company, Philadelphia, Penn. Carved and painted wood with glass, leather, brass and iron attachments. (FC 7-21)

Although the carousel was invented in Europe, it reached its fullest development in the United States between 1870 and 1930. During this time, elaborate carousels became fixtures of the new city parks built for a public with increasing amounts of leisure time and disposable income. Hundreds of park carousels were built by highly skilled woodcarvers and painters while an even greater number of smaller, portable carousels were made for use at country fairs and carnivals.

Shelburne owns examples of both types of carousels: a small, portable machine operates outside the Circus Building, while the animals, chariots and painted panels from a park carousel manufactured by the Gustav Dentzel Company of Philadelphia are exhibited inside the Circus Building. Figures by a number of other manufacturers, both European and American, also are exhibited in the Circus Building.

The German-born Dentzel opened America's first carousel business in 1867. Dentzel's shop produced the most realistic and graceful of all carousel animals; his carvers paid enormous attention to anatomical detail and his painters rendered every nuance of the animals' coloration. Shelburne's Dentzels are from a forty-animal carousel completed about 1902. The three-row machine carried twenty-nine horses and four chariots; menagerie figures include three giraffes, three goats, three deer, a lion and a tiger. The figures were finish-carved by Daniel Muller, the most skilled of Dentzel's craftspeople. All the animals are in their original factory paint, almost unheard of for carousel figures because most carousels were repainted frequently as part of routine maintenance. Several of the figures have recently been conserved; layers of discolored, non-original linseed oil were removed to reveal the richly colored and complex paint patterns applied by Dentzel's masterful painters. All forty animals will eventually receive the same professional treatment.

The small, portable carousel outside the Circus Building was made about 1920 by the Allan Herschell Company of North Tonawanda, New York. In 1883, Herschell began producing carousels designed to endure hard wear and frequent travel. The horses were smaller and more compact than those made for permanent park carousels by such companies as Dentzel and the Philadelphia Toboggan Co. Heads and legs were tucked close to the bodies to minimize breakage and the machines could be easily taken apart, moved and reassembled.
R.S.

Exhibited in: Circus Building

C A R O U S E L   F I G U R E S

Ceramic pitchers,
c. 1790-1830. Various
manufacturers, England.
Creamware with metallic
oxide and decorative
glazes.

Standing cow with
milkmaid and seated
calf, mid-19th century.
Maker unknown,
England. Pearlware
with handpainted
decoration. (31.10.1-88)

Plate, late
18th
century.
Maker
unknown,
England.
Salt-glazed
stoneware
with pierced
and
impressed
decoration.
(31.4-50)

Water cooler,
1830.
I. Seymour,
Troy, N.Y.
Salt-glazed
stoneware
with cobalt
decoration.
(31.8-88)

Ceramic wares made of clay, often glazed with metallic oxides that formed a glassy surface, have been in use since prehistoric times. Their efficiency as food preparation and storage vessels compensated for their fragility, and pottery traditions with distinctive forms, materials and surface decoration developed in Asia, Europe and America before European presence. By the late 17th century, trade and travel linked Asia and Europe, and for the next two hundred years competing manufacturers flooded the English and American market with wares of unprecedented variety and beauty.

Shelburne's broad collection of ceramics includes most types of wares made or used in America from 1700 to 1900. Extensive exhibits of ceramics, including English Staffordshire and mochaware and Chinese export porcelain, may be seen in the Variety Unit. American stoneware and Vermont-made Rockingham are exhibited in the Dutton House, while English and American stoneware and redware may be seen in the Museum's other early homes.

Chinese porcelain was introduced to Europe late in the 17th century, along with the custom of drinking tea. As drinking tea became popular at all levels of society, attractively decorated tablewares became an essential part of the well-furnished household, and throughout the 18th and 19th centuries manufacturers in Western Europe and England competed to produce ceramics designed to resemble Chinese porcelain. The Chinese export porcelain exhibited in the Variety Unit exemplifies the standard to which European manufacturers aspired.

The earliest European imitation of porcelain, tin-glazed earthenware, originated in the Middle East. Manufactured in France and Germany as faience and in Spain, Portugal and Italy as majolica, to English and American consumers purchasing from Holland the ware was commonly known as delft. Low-cost tin-glazed earthenware was widely available but chipped easily, and it was supplanted by sturdier wares. The large tobacco jars in the Variety Unit are decorated in the popular oriental style.

Creamware, a fine grade of earthenware, was developed in England by about 1740. Elaborate formal dinner services with specialized serving dishes were designed for the affluent, while modestly priced undecorated or simply decorated creamware was mass-produced for the middle classes in England and America. Thomas Whieldon produced dappled green, ochre and purple "tortoiseshell" and marbleized glazes, while Josiah Wedgwood experimented with tinted bodies and applied molded deco-

Hong bowl, c. 1780. Maker unknown, China. Porcelain with colored enamel decoration. Gift of George G. Frelinghuysen. (31.14-50)

"Commodore Macdonough's Victory" teapot, c. 1820. Enoch Wood & Sons, England. Pearlware with blue transfer-printed decoration. (31.3-24)

Rockingham ceramics, mid-19th century. Various manufacturers, Bennington, Vt.

Mochaware, mid-19th century. Various manufacturers, England. Creamware with colored slips and engine-turned decoration. Bequest of Harry T. Peters, Jr.

C E R A M I C S

ration. Whieldon ceramics can be seen in the Vermont House, and pierced creamware in the Memorial Building as well as in the Variety Unit.

Pearlware was created in 1779 by adding cobalt to the lead glaze of creamware, which yielded a blue tint more closely resembling porcelain. Much of the transfer-printed china manufactured for the American market between 1790 and 1830 is pearlware. The variety of decorative techniques found in the Museum's encyclopedic ceramic exhibits includes not only the familiar blue and white transfer-printed wares, but arrays of hand-decorated sponge or spatterware, sprig and lusterwares as well as the technologically innovative engine-turned mochaware. The Museum's massive Staffordshire trade-sign pitchers feature some of the manufacturers' most outstanding tableware patterns.

While tablewares were imported well into the 19th century, American production dates back to the mid-17th century. English buff-bodied earthenwares with combed or trailed slip decoration can be seen in the kitchen of the Vermont House; American potters used redware clay to produce similar utilitarian wares until the mid-19th century when redware was supplanted by the familiar gray or buff salt-glazed stoneware with cobalt decoration which can be seen in the Harvest Room of the Dutton House.

By the mid-19th century, mass-production techniques and improved networks of canals, steamboats and railroads allowed American manufacturers to develop the full range of ceramic wares for the expanding middle-class market. Rockingham ware in the Harvest Room of the Dutton House tells this story well: the dappled glaze is reminiscent of fine English Whieldon ware. The available forms range from utilitarian mixing bowls and kitchenwares to decorative and whimsical sculpture.

While the strength of the Shelburne Museum collection is in utilitarian and fine tablewares, figural ceramics should not be overlooked. Staffordshire animal figures and whimsical Toby jugs can be seen in the Variety Unit; upstairs, a magnificent pair of Chelsea swans represents the English figural ceramic tradition at its best. At the other end of the economic spectrum, and one step away from ceramic technology, are the unfired, simple, hand-decorated plaster figures known as chalkware, which provided a decorative touch in less affluent homes.
E.B.

Exhibited in: Dutton House, Electra Havemeyer Webb Memorial Building, General Store, Prentis House, Stencil House, Stone Cottage, Variety Unit, Vermont House

Elephant herd, Roy Arnold
Circus Parade, c. 1925-1955.
West Springfield, Mass. Wood,
paint, metal, leather and cloth.
(56-246)

Circus poster, c. 1925. Erie Litho. Co., Erie, Pa. Lithograph. (27.4-184)

CIRCUS CARVINGS, MINIATURES & POSTERS

The coming of the circus was an annual event awaited with great anticipation in 19th- and early 20th-century America. Weeks before the circus was due, colorful posters appeared on barns and fences, announcing the dates and new performers. Finally, the circus arrived. Excitement grew as wagons, elephants and clowns paraded through town and the big-top tent was raised.

Traveling circuses are represented at the Shelburne Museum by the vintage advertising posters that line the inside wall of the Circus Building. The Museum's collection of over five hundred circus posters is among the finest and most comprehensive in the country. It includes many extremely rare, early posters as well as examples from all the major circuses of the Golden Age of the American traveling circus (c. 1870-1940), including Barnum and Bailey, Ringling Brothers, Adam Forepaugh, John B. Doris and Sells Brothers. The posters are typically brightly colored and attention-grabbing. Most feature dramatic new acts or exotic animals; many make outrageous (and sometimes utterly false) claims—the largest, the smallest, the most dangerous, the rarest, the one and only, etc.

Shelburne owns three elaborate carved miniature circuses. The Circus Parade, which runs over five hundred feet through the Circus Building, was begun in 1925 by Roy Arnold of Hardwick, Vermont. Built on a one-inch to one-foot scale, the parade required thirty years to complete. Four other skilled woodcarvers worked with Mr. Arnold on the parade, which features accurate reproductions of wagons used by circuses of the Golden Age. The miniature parade is complemented by exhibits of pony-sized wagons and several life-sized figures originally carved by Samuel Robb for Barnum and Bailey tableau wagons in the 1890s. Robb is best known for his trade figures, several of which are exhibited in the Stage Coach Inn.

The Kirk Bros. Miniature Circus is a complete three-ringed folk art circus created by Edgar Kirk of Harrisburg, Pennsylvania, over a period of nearly fifty years. Mr. Kirk, who worked as a brakeman on the Pennsylvania railroad, began the circus in 1910 when his children were small and continued to work on it long after they were grown. Working at night after twelve-hour days with the railroad, Mr. Kirk cut the figures for his circus from scrap lumber on a treadle-operated jigsaw and completed the carving with an ordinary penknife. Only the nails and paint were specially purchased. The Kirk circus, complete with animal acts, clowns, trapeze artists, bands, side shows and bleachers full of spectators and vendors,

"Christopher Columbus" circus wagon figure, c. 1886. Samuel A. Robb, New York City. Carved wood and traces of original paint. (FC 10)

Sinbad the Sailor tableau wagon, c. 1940. Roy Arnold, Springfield, Mass. Carved and painted wood, leather and metals. (56-36.1-6)

The Kirk Bros. Miniature Circus, c. 1910-1956. Edgar Decker Kirk, Harrisburg, Pa. Carved and painted wood, tin, iron and leather. Gift of Richard and Joy Kanter. (56-2)

is a monument to Mr. Kirk's creativity, ingenuity and lifelong passion for the circus.

Also on exhibit are scale models of a canal boat circus. From 1882 to 1887, residents of ports along the Erie and Oswego canals of central New York state were visited each summer by Sig Sautelle's Big Shows, one of the only circuses ever to travel by boat. Sautelle, born George Satterlee (1848-1928), was a colorful showman and one of the most successful promoters of his time. The wooden models of Sautelle's two circus canal boats, built by Milo Smith of Herkimer, New York, provide a vivid picture of this unique regional circus.
R.S.

Exhibited in: Circus Building

Fleece mittens, c. 1860-1880s. Maker unknown, New England. Knitted wool yarn embroidered with fleece pile. Gift of Mrs. R. E. Simpson. (15-34.3)

Hats and bonnets, c. 1890-1930s. Makers unknown, New England and New York. Straw, feathers and silk velvet ribbons.

Two-piece garden party dress, c. 1898. Maker unknown, Burlington, Vt. Pleated and tucked cotton mull fabric, trimmed with black beaded lace and velvet ribbon. Gift of Early Wingate. Hat, c. 1900. Maker unknown, Manchester, Vt. Tuscany straw, trimmed with ribbon and silk flowers. Gift of Paul Hart. Parasol, c. 1890s. Maker unknown, Northeastern United States. Black machine-made lace over black silk with carved wood handle. (14-528, 13-151, 14.5-53)

CLOTHING AND ACCESSORIES

Clothing in its simplest form protects the body. As regional cultures emerged, each developed its own distinctive costume traditions based on climate and locally available materials. Travelers began exchanging information on styles and fabrics, and on weaving, embroidery and lacemaking techniques. Soon growing middle and upper classes were able to afford garments fashioned for beauty as well as utility. Clothing styles became more elaborate and began to reflect gender roles, social and economic position in society, and even occupations.

Shelburne's collection of over eight hundred men's, women's and children's costume pieces dates from the late 17th to early 20th centuries. The costumes illustrate the variety of styles worn, the fabrics used and the plain and fancy sewing skills practiced by women in urban and rural areas.

In the 18th and 19th centuries, American women learned about and copied the latest European styles from travelers or from "fashion dolls" sent by French and English fashion designers. Women's magazines, first published in the early 19th century, also illustrated the latest costume styles, fabrics, and colors. Americans often adapted European fashions to the needs of life in America.

Women sewed clothes themselves, with the help of a relative or friend, or hired a seamstress. Fabric was expensive and most women of modest means wore simple shirts, skirts or dresses for everyday wear and saved a more formal dress for church and paying calls. Dresses and other articles of clothing often were passed down through the family and remade as styles changed.

Hats were an important fashion accessory; white caps were worn indoors, hats or bonnets outside. Cloaks and shawls and short jackets were worn for warmth. Women carried decorative parasols for protection against the sun and as a fashion accessory. Valuables and papers were carried in slim folded pocketbooks of leather or embroidered fabric and later in small bags with draw-string tops called reticules.

Shelburne's clothing and accessories are exhibited in the Hat and Fragrance Textile Gallery on a rotating basis and are often included in such special Museum programs as "Christmas at the Shelburne Museum," "Lilac Sunday" and "Farm Day." American Indian clothing exhibited in the Beach Lodge and Gallery illustrates early types of garments that remained in use until the late 19th century.
C.Y.O.

Exhibited in: Hat and Fragrance, Variety Unit, Webb Gallery

Clothing and Accessories

CLOTHING AND ACCESSORIES

Red-throated loon, c. 1900. Maker unknown, Maine or Nova Scotia. Carved and painted wood, tawhide.

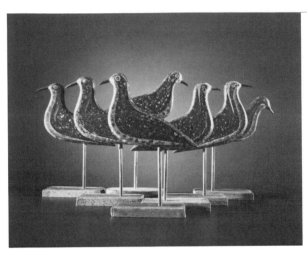

Golden plovers, c. 1870. Makers unknown, Nantucket, Mass. Carved and painted wood.

Two decorative yellowlegs, c. 1930. A. Elmer Crowell, E. Harwich, Mass. Carved and painted wood, glass eyes, tin wing tip, iron legs. Gift of Mrs. Stuart Crocker. (26.2-23, 24)

Wildfowl decoys, made to lure game birds to within shooting range, have been used by American hunters for centuries. American Indians originated the idea over a thousand years ago in response to the abundance of the continent's wild game. The earliest decoys made by whites were probably carved in the late 1700s. The idea spread rapidly and by 1840 the wooden decoy was firmly established in American hunting tradition.

Following the Civil War, improved transportation systems, more advanced weapons, and abundant game combined to create what has been called the greatest wildfowl hunt in the history of the world. Professional market gunners worked in most areas, supplying game to meet intense public demand. Well-made decoys were among the tools most vital to their trade. To meet the needs of the market gunners and the many well-to-do sportsmen who traveled from the cities to shoot birds, scores of craftsmen turned to decoy-making full time. Just before 1900, such firms as Mason's Decoy Factory of Detroit, which employed a number of carvers working from the same patterns, offered decoys by mail order. Federal conservation legislation brought the market-gunning era to an end just after World War I. However, sportsmen continued to hunt over wooden decoys until after World War II, when inexpensive molded plastic decoys took over the marketplace.

Shelburne's collection of nearly nine hundred working decoys, housed in the Dorset House, is the finest and most comprehensive public collection in the world. It contains superb examples by master craftsmen from all over North America, including A. Elmer Crowell—whose wide variety of working decoys, decorative carvings and miniatures prove him to be the most versatile of the old-time masters — and such well-known carvers as Bill Bowman, Lee Dudley, Nathan Cobb, Lem and Steve Ward, Joseph Lincoln, Albert Laing, Shang Wheeler, George Warin and John Blair. There is also a small collection of fish decoys, used by ice fishermen to lure pike, muskellunge and other predators within spearing range.

Every major hunting area in North America produced decoys. Differences in hunting methods and water conditions affected local decoy-making traditions, and dozens of regional variations developed. Exhibits in the Dorset House are arranged by region to allow easy comparison of the treatment of like species by carvers from different regions and, more subtly, within regions. Maine decoys, for example, as seen in the work of Gus Wilson, are typically solid-bodied with wide, flat bottoms and simple paint patterns. By contrast, Illinois decoys, such as

Red-breasted merganser, c. 1930. Nathan Rowley Horner, West Creek, N.J. (FD18-6)

Canada goose decoy, c. 1849-1870. Attributed to Charles C. Osgood, Salem, Mass. Carved and painted wood, glass eyes, brass plate joining neck and body. Gift of Mrs. P. H. B. Frelinghuysen. (FD 2-34)

Wildfowl decoys, c. 1890-1930. Various makers, North America. Carved and painted wood, glass eyes.

those made by Robert and Catherine Elliston, are hollow-bodied with rounded bottoms and elaborately detailed paint. Other regional styles, including those of Louisiana, Virginia, the Chesapeake Bay, New Jersey, Long Island, Connecticut, Quebec and Ontario, are equally distinctive.

In addition to decoys, many carvers also crafted miniatures and decorative birds. Elmer Crowell of Cape Cod was a pioneer in these areas. He offered his customers what he called a "songless aviary," producing miniature songbirds, shorebirds and ducks in sets of twenty-five species and also creating many life-sized decorative carvings of birds and fish. A wide variety of Crowell's work, including a heron used as a garden ornament, several wall-mounted flying birds and nearly a hundred miniatures, is exhibited in the Dorset House. Miniatures and decorative carvings by such other masters as Lem Ward, A.J. King and Harold Haertel are also on exhibit. *R.S.*

Exhibited in: Dorset House

(Left to right) English queen doll, c. 1780-1820. Maker unknown. Wood. English queen doll, c. 1780-1820. Maker unknown. Wood. American doll, c. 1870. Maker unknown. Rubber and cloth. (20.11-87, 20.11-102, 20.3-192)

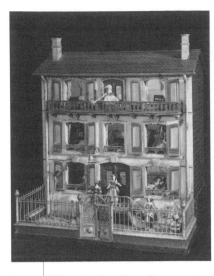

"Female Seminary" dollhouse, c. 1870. Maker unknown, France, furnished by Helen Bruce, c. 1955. (30.1-15)

Girl dolls, c. 1875. Izannah Walker, Central Falls, R.I. Painted molded-cloth heads, cloth bodies and costumes. (20.3-193 & 194)

Dolls reflect the time and culture in which they were made; many may be viewed as miniature three-dimensional portraits offering insight into past eras.

Shelburne's collection of over a thousand dolls is exhibited on the second floor of the Variety Unit. Complementing the dolls are twenty-seven doll houses and nearly twelve hundred doll accessories that echo in miniature the Museum's collections of buildings, furniture, ceramics, hatboxes and household furnishings. Most of Shelburne's dollhouses were decorated by Electra Havemeyer Webb, who filled the rooms by juxtaposing miniature objects she had collected (including prints and paintings) with furnishings specifically made for dollhouses.

Many American dolls of the 18th and 19th centuries were made at home of readily available materials, including wood, rags, clay, dried apples, corn husks, bottles and clay pipes. Until World War I, the majority of dolls sold in America were imported from England, France and Germany. Joel Ellis of Springfield, Vermont, made some of the first commercial American dolls with wooden bodies, patented jointed limbs, and pewter hands and feet. Izannah Walker of Rhode Island made cloth dolls with handpainted faces and hair. Examples by both Ellis and Walker are in the Variety Unit.

Not all dolls were playthings. In the late 1800s, French dollmakers such as Bru, Jumeau and Steiner, and German dollmakers such as Kestner and Simon & Halbig—all represented in Shelburne's collections—created elegant bisque-head dolls with large, wide glass eyes, thick eyebrows, long lashes, cupid's bow lips, beautifully coifed real hair and elaborate dresses of silk and other fine fabrics. Also of European origin is a group of automata, including a monkey drummer, magician, opium smoker and woman at her toilette. These rare mechanical dolls all move their heads and limbs when wound.

Souvenir and keepsake dolls were popular products in many areas frequented by tourists. Dolls created entirely of different sizes and shapes of shells, for example, come from a number of French and English resort towns; a number of these fragile dolls may be seen in the Hat and Fragrance Textile Gallery. English peddler dolls, which depict street vendors and their diverse wares, and American Indian dolls, complete with bead-decorated costumes, are exhibited in the Variety Unit.
R.S.

Exhibited in: Hat and Fragrance Textile Gallery, Toy Shop, Variety Unit

DOLLS, DOLLHOUSES & MINIATURES

Dolls, Dollhouses and Miniatures

Armchair, c. 1770. Maker unknown, branded "HK." Walnut and pine. Gift of George Frelinghuysen. (3.3-239)

Tea Table, c. 1750. Maker unknown, possibly from Connecticut. Cherry and maple. (3.6-81)

High chest of drawers, c. 1780. Maker unknown, Norwich, Vt. Yellow birch and pine; red stain. (3.1-15)

Shelburne Museum's furniture collection represents the different styles and tastes of 18th- and 19th-century America. It includes examples of the most sophisticated urban furniture produced in the nation as well as many simpler pieces made by country cabinetmakers for use in rural homes. These country pieces include one of the greatest strengths of Shelburne Museum—its collection of paint-decorated furniture.

Most high style furniture was created in large commercial centers such as Boston, New York, Philadelphia, and Newport, Rhode Island. It was carefully constructed by specialized craftspeople who learned cabinetmaking from skilled masters. Urban cabinetmakers, unlike their rural counterparts, had access to pattern books, fancy imported tropical woods such as mahogany, and finished pieces of furniture brought from Europe by metropolitan merchants to use as models. The Vermont House exhibits a selection of such high style American furniture. In the dining room is a table attributed to John Townsend of Newport, a set of Massachusetts side chairs with pierced backs, and an unusual marble-topped tea table. A Boston high chest "Japanned" in imitation of oriental lacquer painting may be seen in the parlor. Also of note in the parlor is the desk-and-secretary, made in the lower Connecticut River valley, which manifests its more rural origin in the brass hinges on the doors of the secretary and in the unrefined lines of the case.

Not all Americans could afford to pay for a high style writing desk or dining table. In the early 1800s, rural craftspeople produced utilitarian furniture outside of major urban centers for the emerging middle class. The furniture was less expensive, rarely incorporated fancy woods and often copied the shape and scale of fashionable high style pieces available in Boston or Philadelphia. Styles often traveled slowly to rural areas. The birch and pine high chest on the second floor of the Dutton House, for example, was made in eastern Vermont or western New Hampshire around 1780. The chest's slightly curved legs, elegant corniced top and tall upper case represent an anonymous cabinetmaker's translation and simplification of the Queen Anne style, a style already out of fashion in urban areas.

Because most country furniture was made from plain but readily available wood such as pine, it was often painted to improve its appearance. Examples of grain-painted, sponge-painted and stenciled furniture are on view in the Webb Gallery and in the historic houses. Some furniture was painted in an effort to mimic the distinctive grains of more costly, imported woods. For example, the elaborate painted

Furniture

Chest of drawers, c. 1700-1725. Maker unknown, eastern Massachusetts. Paint-decorated pine. (3.4-2)

Windsor-style armchair, c. 1775-1800. Maker unknown, Rhode Island. Poplar and ash; green paint. Gift of J. Watson Webb, Jr. (3.3-2)

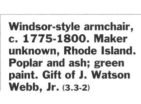

Armchair, 1891-1892. Tiffany Glass and Decorating Company, New York. Ash. Gift of George Frelinghuysen. (3.3-328)

patterns of a pine chest made in South Shaftsbury, Vermont, which may be seen on the lower level of the Webb Gallery, were designed to make viewers believe it was a veneered chest employing fine woods.

Some types of paint decoration were more fanciful. A chest of drawers made in Eastern Massachusetts, also in the Webb Gallery, is decorated with floral vines and painted buildings. Two small tables in the Webb Gallery were decorated with landscape scenes, bowls of fruit and lines of poetry by young women studying at finishing schools. A pair of Massachusetts side chairs in the Webb Gallery were stenciled by William Page Eaton with painted peacocks and flowers. Compare these chairs to the set of stenciled chairs by Ara Howe of Brookfield, Vermont, in the same gallery. Although the form and method of decoration are the same, Howe's chairs are less refined, his stenciling less elaborate. This comparison begins to illustrate the differences between high style and vernacular furniture.

During the American Industrial Revolution (c. 1865-1900), the furniture industry, like every other major industry, was mechanized. Individual craftspeople and designers like Louis Comfort Tiffany, whose work can be seen in the Electra Havemeyer Webb Memorial Building, continued to work for upper class patrons, but inexpensive, factory-made chairs, tables, beds and stands flooded an eager market of middle-class Victorians. The popularity of carved decoration and elaborate upholstery, characteristic of the period, can be seen on the furniture displayed in the parlor of the Lighthouse and on the promenade deck of the Steamer *Ticonderoga*. *L.B.H.*

Exhibited in: Historic Houses, Electra Havemeyer Webb Memorial Building, Lighthouse, *Ticonderoga*, Webb Gallery

Goblets, mid-19th to early 20th centuries. Various manufacturers, United States. Pressed glass. Gift of Elizabeth Garrison.

Bull's-eye window, c. 1820. Burlington Glassworks, Burlington, Vt. Glass with wood sash. (4.2-30 1)

Glassmakers were among the skilled craftspeople who settled in North America during the colonial era. During the 17th century, glass was a luxury. By the late 18th century, German artisans, including Stiegel in Pennsylvania, had established successful glasshouses in the mid-Atlantic colonies; British works were established in Connecticut, Pittsburgh and Boston; and British and Dutch partners founded an enterprise in Albany. Glass factories required sand as a source of silica, and ample wood to heat massive furnaces. Silica combined with the correct proportion of soda or potash and lime produced glass for bottles, windows and decorative objects.

In 18th-century glasshouses, skilled artisans produced free-blown bottles, window glass, and table and decorative wares for affluent households. Utilitarian wares were produced of "green glass" in shades varying from pale aquamarine to deep olive. The green was caused by the presence of impurities in the mixture.

To create free-blown glass, air is blown into a ball of molten glass through a long hollow pipe. The resulting bubble is rolled into a symmetrical form on a slab, then tooled by hand into its final shape. Smaller pieces of glass may be added for handles or stems. Finished vessels might be further decorated by engraving or etching designs into the surface, or by the use of colored enamels. Free-blown window glass was made by transferring the bubble to a rod known as a pontil, and spinning it until the bubble opened into a flat circular sheet. Small rectangular panes were cut from the perimeter. A "bull's-eye" window, formed of the pontil-marked centers from sheets of glass manufactured in Burlington in the early 19th century can be seen in the Variety Unit, along with a full round uncut sheet of window glass; bull's-eye panes may also be seen above the door of the Prentis House.

Mold-blown glass is made by pressing a gather of glass on the end of a pipe into an open mold that establishes the form and may also provide surface decoration, withdrawing it, then blowing it to finished size. In the 19th century, manufacturers developed new techniques for mass producing elaborately decorated surfaces. Pressed glass is made by pouring molten glass into a mold, then using a plunger to force the glass against the mold. Shelburne's collection includes an assortment of molded flasks as well as a wide variety of pressed-glass goblets.

Even after mold-manufacturing techniques became widespread for tablewares, 19th-century glassblowers continued to create colorful whimseys, including hollow rolling pins used for pastry, and

Glass canes, late 19th century. Makers unknown, eastern United States. Blown, pulled and twisted glass rods. (32.1.4-1-43)

Glass dish, c. 1865. Perhaps McKee and Brothers, Philadelphia, Pa. Molded. (32.3.3-3)

Bottles, late 18th to early 19th centuries. Makers unknown, United States. Left to right: free blown, mold blown and pressed glass.

cluding hollow rolling pins used for pastry, and purely decorative canes and "witch balls."

Shelburne's glass collection numbers nearly two thousand pieces dating from 1750 to 1900. Exhibits in the Variety Unit include early free-blown flasks and window glass as well as mold-blown bottles and flasks; pattern glass plates, serving dishes and decorative pieces; colorful canes, rolling pins, marbles, "witch balls" and other whimseys; and miniature glass doll dishes. The Garrison collection of American pattern glass goblets includes eleven hundred patterns; fifty examples are exhibited on a rotating basis. In addition to the above exhibits, a wide range of patent medicine and other bottles may be seen in the General Store and Apothecary Shop.
E.B.

Exhibited in: Apothecary Shop, General Store, Prentis House, Variety Unit

Glass

Hat and bandboxes, c. 1820-1860s. Makers unknown, New England and northeastern United States. Block-printed paper and paste board.

Photograph of Hannah Davis, 1784-1863

Hatbox label, c. 1832. Jaffrey, N.H.

WARRANTED NAILED
BAND BOXES,
MANUFACTURED BY
HANNAH DAVIS,
East Jaffrey, N. H.

Hat and bandboxes, c. 1820-1860s. Makers unknown, New England and northeastern United States. Block-printed paper and paste board.

HAT AND BANDBOXES

Hatboxes and their smaller relation the bandbox were made of thin sheets of bent wood or pasteboard and covered with decorative printed papers. Serving as an inexpensive form of luggage for men and women, the boxes carried and stored hats, collars, cuffs and other finery. Their use increased in the 19th century as new roads, steamboats and steam locomotives encouraged more people to travel.

Shelburne's collection of over two hundred hatboxes and bandboxes, exhibited in the Hat and Fragrance Textile Gallery, is one of the largest and most comprehensive on public display in the country. The exhibit illustrates the wide variety of box sizes and forms, paper colors and designs and is particularly rich in rare, early papers. Museum founder Electra Havemeyer Webb, who assembled the collection over many years, had a great interest in printed patterns and decorative wallpapers.

Most hat-and-bandbox factories were located in larger cities such as New York, Boston, Philadelphia or Hartford. However, many individuals operated small companies to make and sell hatboxes to local markets. One of the best known of these craftspeople is Hannah Davis (1784-1863) of Jaffrey, New Hampshire, whose work is well represented in Shelburne's collection.

Early boxes were covered with printed and handpainted paper imported from England and Europe. Wallpaper from American printers became available in the 19th century and was quickly adopted by hat-and-bandbox makers.

Patterns and colors for the papers were influenced by current decorating styles. The images of classical architecture, griffins and chariots pulled by birds were inspired by the mid-19th century interest in Greek and Roman history. Common and exotic creatures such as cows, beavers, anacondas and giraffes were inspired by zoos, traveling animal exhibitions, illustrated bestiaries and geography books. Finally, hatbox makers often copied illustrations of American city and rural scenes, historic landmarks, new modes of transportation, or important people and events published in popular books and magazines. Popular papers include the New York City Deaf and Dumb Asylum, a duck hunt, a sidewheel steamboat, President Harrison's log cabin and a balloon ascension.
C.Y.O.

Exhibited in: Dutton House, Hat and Fragrance Textile Gallery

Hat and Bandboxes

Cutter, c. 1840.
Maker unknown,
Vermont.
Painted wood
and iron. Gift
of J. K. Byard.
(40-S-25)

Park Phaeton, c. 1900.
Ferdinand French and
Co., Boston, Mass.
Wood, iron, leather,
cloth. Gift of Arthur
Brown. (40-V-24)

Patent medicine wagon,
c. 1895. Maker unknown,
Abbott, Maine. Painted
wood and iron. (40-W-35)

HORSE-DRAWN VEHICLES

Carriages and coaches began to be widely used in Britain during the 17th century. However, real progress in carriage building was not made until the late 1700s, when Royal Mail coach service began. For the first time many carriages were designed for comfort and speed and were made alike, using interchangeable parts. Soon carriage driving became the fashionable way to travel, although for many years the cost of vehicles restricted their use primarily to the nobility and upper classes.

The manufacture of horse-drawn vehicles advanced more quickly in 19th-century America, where vehicles quickly became available to people of every social class. By the late 1800s, American coach builders had even developed light and practical vehicles that were available to the general public at low prices through mail order houses such as Sears and Roebuck. An elegant runabout made by Brewster and Company, America's finest coach builder, cost $425 in 1900; a runabout sold by Sears was $24.95.

Shelburne's Horseshoe Barn and its neighboring Annex exhibit 19th- and early 20th-century horse-drawn vehicles, including carriages, farm and trade wagons, stagecoaches and sleighs. Early firefighting equipment is exhibited in the Shaker Shed. Almost every type of vehicle used in New England in the 1800s is represented within these collections. One of the most comprehensive in the country—numbering 225—Shelburne's collection is particularly important because most of the vehicles retain their original upholstery, lamps and decorative finishes.

Many of Shelburne's finest vehicles originally belonged to Dr. William Seward Webb, father-in-law of the Museum's founder, Electra Havemeyer Webb. An outstanding group of Dr. Webb's vehicles may be seen on the second floor of the Horseshoe Barn. These include a number of elegant carriages and coaches by New York's Brewster and Company and a remarkable pair of custom-made vehicles—a caleche and a satin-trimmed berlin—by Million et Guiet of Paris.

Rural Americans were often too busy to travel during the warm months, when farm chores kept them close to home. Winter brought more time to travel. Snow could be packed down with horse-drawn rollers to form a far smoother surface than was available on dirt roads at other times of the year. Sleighs were much easier to build and repair than wheeled vehicles; a home craftsperson without specialized training could construct and maintain them. For these reasons, the typical northern farm family

Horse-drawn Vehicles

Victoria sleigh, c. 1886. Brewster and Co., New York City. Iron, wood and cloth. Gift of the Webb Family in memory of Dr. and Mrs. Seward Webb. (40-S-31)

Interior, Berlin, c. 1890. Millon et Guiet, Paris, France. Satin upholstery. Gift of the Webb Family in memory of Dr . and Mrs. Seward Webb. (40-V-48)

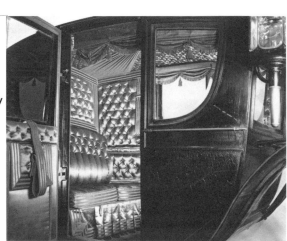

Berlin, c. 1890. Millon et Guiet, Paris, France. Iron, painted wood, brass, glass, cloth. Gift of the Webb Family in memory of Dr. and Mrs. Seward Webb. (40-V-48)

owned three sleighs for every wheeled vehicle it kept.

Sleighs echoed wheeled vehicles in form; some wheeled vehicles, like the hearse exhibited in the Horseshoe Barn Annex, could be converted from wheels to runners as the seasons changed. Sleighs in the Horseshoe Barn range from small and simple homemade wooden cutters to elaborate, multi-passenger surreys, caleches and victorias. The collection also includes a stage sleigh, a schoolbus sleigh, a butcher's delivery sleigh and a police ambulance and paddy wagon sleigh.

Multi-passenger stagecoaches and omnibuses provided public transportation for travelers within and between cities, from train stations to hotels, and on sight seeing trips. Businesses transported goods by horse, often using wagons and sleighs that advertised their wares with decorative pictures and signage. Commercial vehicles in the Horseshoe Barn Annex include a Concord Coach used to transport hotel guests in the White Mountains, a butcher's wagon complete with hanging scales and meat hooks, a Maine druggist's patent medicine wagon and a Pennsylvania Conestoga wagon, used to haul produce from rural farms to city markets.

Vehicles were also essential to firefighters, who needed to transport water and equipment quickly. A variety of early firefighting vehicles are exhibited at the Shaker Shed. The horse was a latecomer to firefighting, not pressed widely into service until the 1870s. To save precious time, horses were kept in the firehouse. Their stalls had break-away chains and, at the sound of the alarm, the horses raced to their places in front of the waiting equipment. Their collars and harnesses were suspended from the ceiling, poised like spiders in a web, ready to drop at a touch.

The steam-driven pumper, the hose wagon and the hook-and-ladder truck became the three major horse-drawn firefighting vehicles. However, it was the steamer, usually driven with horses harnessed two- or three-abreast, that provided the most spectacular sight as it flew down the street with smoke pouring from the funnel of its boiler, building up a head of steam to run the pumps.
R.S.

Exhibited in: Horseshoe Barn, Horsehoe Barn Annex, Shaker Shed

Bedtickings, bolster covers and furnishing fabric yardage, c. 1800-1840s. Makers unknown, Pennsylvania and New England. Handwoven cotton and linen.

Show towel, c. 1790-1810. Maker unknown, marked "C.H.," possibly from Pennsylvania. Linen plain weave with overshot pattern bands. (11.1-29.1)

Pheasant and flowers counterpane, c. late 18th century. Maker unknown, found on Long Island, N.Y. Resist block-printed linen. (10-121)

HOUSEHOLD TEXTILES

Shelburne Museum's large and varied collection of household textiles represents work made and used in America from the late 18th to the mid-20th centuries.

Before textile production was mechanized during the Industrial Revolution in the early 19th century, all cloth was handwoven on large "barn-frame" looms by families at home or by professional weavers in a shop. Cloth was labor-intensive to produce, expensive, and highly prized. The wealth of the household dictated the type, quality and quantity of the textiles used. Families provided themselves first with clothing, bedding, bedcovers and towels. Tablecovers, curtains and floor covers were often considered a luxury and acquired later.

Bedlinens, including sheets, pillow cases, and bolsters, were typically woven in plain weave of linen or cotton and were often marked with the owner's name and inventory number. Towels for everyday use were made of heavy plain-weave linen and cotton cloth. Decorative show towels and tablecovers were woven in white with figured diamond or lace patterns, embroidered and finished with knit, crocheted or net lace and fringe.

As a family's wealth increased, bedhangings, bedskirts, window curtains and furniture covers were added to the household inventory. Although checked, solid-colored and plaid fabrics were commonly used, imported fabrics with copperplate- and woodblock-printed floral and geometric designs were also bought for wealthier homes.

Examples of early handweaving; Jacquard-woven textiles; stenciled, resist-printed and dyed fabrics; and woodblock-, copperplate- and roller-printed goods are exhibited in the Hat and Fragrance Textile Gallery as well as in the Museum historic homes. Handweaving and spinning tools including a Jacquard loom are exhibited and demonstrated in the Weaving Shop.
C.Y.O.

Exhibited in: Hat and Fragrance Textile Gallery, Historic Houses, Weaving Shop

Household Textiles

Clockjack, c. 1750-1800. Maker unknown, originally used in the Golden Ball Tavern, Weston, Mass. Cast and wrought iron, wood. (35.17-3)

Knife and fork, c. 1780-1850. Maker unknown, northeastern United States. Wrought iron and bone.

Frying pan, kettle, and cookpot, c. 1800-1850. Makers unknown, northeastern United States. Cast and wrought iron.

HOUSEHOLD TOOLS

Housekeeping chores in 18th- and 19th-century America went far beyond the basic cooking, cleaning, and laundry work familiar to most families today. In addition to those tasks, women and children hauled water from the well, dipped and molded tallow candles from rendered animal fat, spun wool and flax, wove cloth, sewed and mended clothes for the family and made lye soap. Although some tools made the work easier, all these tasks were labor intensive and time consuming. In early America a woman's work was truly "never done."

Before 1850, when wood cookstoves came into general use, all cooking was done over open hearth fires. Cast-iron pots and kettles were suspended over the flames for cooking or set on trivets before the fire for warming. Meat grills and toasters were used over a bed of coals. Meat and poultry were roasted in tin reflector ovens, covered iron pots or on standing racks or revolving spits turned by mechanical clock jacks. Bread was mixed in huge bowls, set in wooden dough trays to rise, and placed in the fireplace oven with a peel, a long-handled tool like a flat shovel.

Shelburne's laundry equipment makes clear that washing clothes for a family was hard work. Clothes were soaked in wash tubs of boiling water, scrubbed against corrugated wood, metal, or ceramic wash boards, then dried outdoors on rope lines or indoors on racks. Pants, socks and gloves were often stretched taut over wooden forms to prevent wrinkles. Irons, made of solid cast iron and brass, were heated in the fire or on top of the stove and used to smooth out wrinkles and set pleats. These heavy sad irons (so-called for their heavy weight, as was the popular definition of "sad" during this period) were replaced in the 1850s by lighter, hollow irons that could be filled with hot coals.

Shelburne's extensive collection of household equipment reflects the variety of specialized tools necessary to care for a house and family in early America. Household tools are prominent in the kitchens and pantries of the Museum's historic houses, and a variety of implements and labor-saving devices are exhibited in the Shaker Shed. Crafted from wood, tin, brass and iron, many are decorated with carved surfaces and paint. Washing and ironing equipment may be seen in the Sawyer's Cabin, Shaker Shed and other historic houses.
C.Y.O.

Exhibited in: Dutton House, Prentis House, Sawyers Cabin, Shaker Shed, Stencil House, Stone Cottage

Household Tools

Thumb latch, c. 1840. Maker unknown, Vermont. Wrought iron.

Eel spear, c. 1840-1870. Maker unknown, New York or New England. Wrought iron. (45.3-8)

Parlor stove, c. 1840. G. H. Iron Co., Brandon, Vt. Cast iron. Gift of David Wells. (65.8-9)

Iron ore was one of the first and most important resources discovered in America. It was mined in many areas in the American colonies and its extraction and processing created one of the young country's first industries.

After the ore was extracted, it had to be refined into pig iron by mixing it with lime and charcoal and smelting it in a furnace. The first successful American iron works for processing iron ore was established in 1643 on the Saugus River in Massachusetts. Other iron manufacturing centers were established in Connecticut, Rhode Island, Pennsylvania and New Jersey in the 1670s and were in operation in five additional colonies by 1750.

Workers in the iron foundries crafted wood and metal patterns and used molten pig iron to cast such things as stoves, kettles and pans, andirons and trivets. In the 19th century, ornamental castings such as gates, hitching posts, weathervanes and garden statuary also were produced.

While pig iron was suitable for casting, it was too impure to be worked by blacksmiths. Malleable wrought iron for blacksmithing was produced by further refining pig iron in open forges called fineries. Working by hand at forges like the one at Shelburne's Blacksmith Shop, blacksmiths wrought hearth implements, household utensils from forks to candle holders, hand and farm tools, and hardware such as door hinges and latches.

Shelburne's extensive collection of early American wrought and cast iron includes a wide variety of forms. A large cast eagle sits outside the Museum Store; other cast sculptures are exhibited in the Stagecoach Inn. Cast hitching posts stand outside the Stagecoach Inn and the Horseshoe Barn. Inside the Barn and Annex, skillfull ironwork may be seen on the horse-drawn vehicles.

Cast-iron stoves, with tight fireboxes that burned wood or coal much more efficiently than open hearth fireplaces, became a popular heating source in the 1830s and were a fixture in most New England homes in the second half of the 19th century. Several cast-iron parlor stoves, including an elaborately decorated model with four fluted Greek Revival-style columns above the firebox, are exhibited in the Shaker Shed.

Skilled blacksmiths sometimes added decorative elements to such basic hardware as door hinges and latches. Attractively shaped early wrought iron latches and hinges grace many of the Museum's historic structures. A particularly fine thumblatch made by a local blacksmith opens the door to the Stone

Ironware

Blacksmith's and farrier's tools and horseshoe, c. 1870-1920. Makers unknown, United States. Iron and wood.

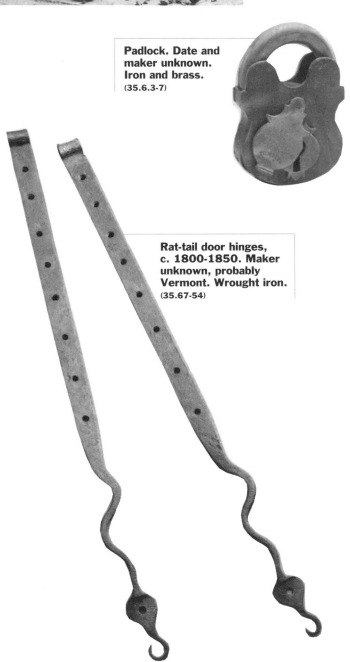

Padlock. Date and maker unknown. Iron and brass. (35.6.3-7)

Rat-tail door hinges, c. 1800-1850. Maker unknown, probably Vermont. Wrought iron. (35.67-54)

Cottage, moved from South Burlington, Vermont. This and other latches offer a rare chance to appreciate Museum objects through touch. Massive strap hinges are especially noticeable on the doors of the Horseshoe Barn Annex, the Weaving Shop and the Printing Shop. Many other hand-wrought latches and hinges are exhibited in the Shaker Shed.

Also on the second floor of the Shaker Shed are a number of iron kitchen implements, including cast kettles and pans and hand-wrought trivets, forks, toasters and roasting spits. Similar objects fill the hearths of all the Museum's historic houses, especially that of the large Dutton House kitchen. Also in the Dutton House is a wrought iron cradle made by a Brandon, Vermont, blacksmith. The Windsor-style cradle is constructed with mortise-and-tenon joints, like those a woodworker would use. A wooden Windsor cradle made by a Vermont chairmaker also is exhibited in the Dutton House and offers a fascinating comparison.
R.S.

Exhibited in: Blacksmith Shop, Dutton House, Horseshoe Barn, Horseshoe Barn Annex, Shaker Shed, Stagecoach Inn, Stone Cottage

Ironware

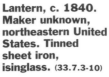

Lantern, c. 1840. Maker unknown, northeastern United States. Tinned sheet iron, isinglass. (33.7.3-10)

Rushlight holder, c. 1800. Maker unknown, northeastern United States. Wrought iron, ash burl stand. (33.1-10)

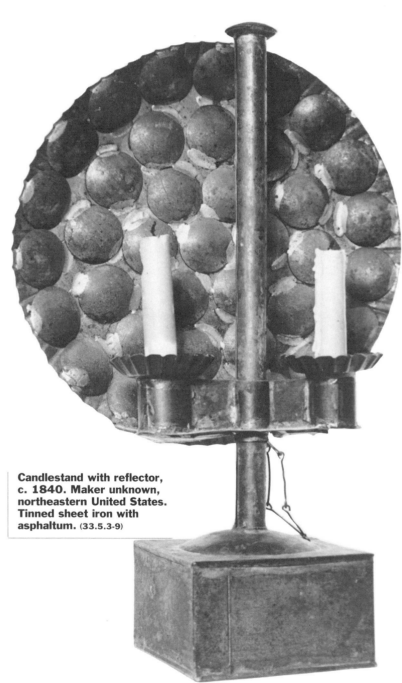

Candlestand with reflector, c. 1840. Maker unknown, northeastern United States. Tinned sheet iron with asphaltum. (33.5.3-9)

Lighting was dim in the early American home. People rose, worked and went to bed with the sun, as it provided the only satisfactory light. Until about 1800, candles made at home from the tallow of slaughtered cattle were the primary artificial light source in the home. Many candleholders, especially those made of tin, included reflecting devices to magnify the meager light offered by the candle. Lanterns, often made of pierced tin, shielded candles for outside use. Candles made from waxy bayberries or spermaceti, a fatty substance from the head of the sperm whale, smelled and burned better than tallow. However, gathering berries was painstaking and time-consuming work, and even George Washington complained about the price of spermaceti candles.

Early settlers in New England sometimes used the stalk of the meadow rush as a candle. Rushes, which grow in wet areas, were gathered in late August. The stems were cut into eight- to ten-inch lengths, the outer, fibrous layer was peeled off, the remaining porous pith soaked in lard or tallow. After drying, the rush was placed in a wrought iron holder at a 45-degree angle. Like a candle, the rushlight was lit at its upper end; it had to be shifted up periodically as it burned.

Colonial settlers also often used small grease lamps with wicks. Larger and more sophisticated lamps became available in the late 1700s. Whale oil, obtained by boiling down blubber, was an important lamp fuel from the late 1700s through the 1850s, when inexpensive petroleum-based kerosene was introduced.

The Museum has a large, diverse collection of early lighting devices, including candlesticks and candelabras, rushlight holders, lanterns and grease lamps. The second floor of the Shaker Shed holds a large group of these, as well as candle molds and a rotating candle-dipping stand. Other examples of lighting devices can be seen in the context of Shelburne's historic houses.
R.S.

Exhibited in: Dutton House, Prentis House, Sawyer's Cabin, Shaker Shed, Stencil House, Stone Cottage, Vermont House

Lighting Devices

Embroidered stumpwork needlework, c. 17th century. Maker unknown, marked "S.W.," Great Britain. Gold and silver wire, silk and wool yarns on linen canvas. (8.3-23)

Detail, embroidered bedhanging, c. 1780-1800. Maker unknown, New England. Wool yarn on linen fabric. Gift of Katharine Prentis Murphy. (8.1-70)

Table set, late 19th century. Maker unknown, United States. Cotton lawn fabric, drawn work and embroidery.

Sewing was an essential skill for any woman in 18th- and 19th-century America, and for a young woman, was considered the most important accomplishment. Shelburne's collection of American and English plain sewing, marking and fancy embroidery work illustrates the variety of needlework produced by women of all ages from the 17th to the 20th centuries.

Before sewing machines became affordable and widely available in the mid-19th century, every article of clothing and household textile was stitched by hand. Girls as young as three years old were taught to use a needle. They began with simple stitching involved in hemming and constructing clothing and bedcovers; more complicated embroidery came next.

Young girls used simple cross-stitiches to embroider samplers with alphabets, numerals, floral designs and verses to practice basic stitches. As their skills improved, they included animals, houses, flowers, poetic verse, and flowering borders, as well as their name, age and the date. Later they used the same cross-stitching technique to mark household linens and clothing for identification and inventory.

Sewing was also learned outside the home. American female academies, established in the late 18th and 19th centuries, included lessons in needlework as an important part of their curriculum. Silkwork pictures of landscapes, houses, biblical scenes and verses were intended to be framed and displayed in the girls' homes. As they studied geography, they embroidered detailed maps of their state, country and the world. Family records were embroidered with charts of family births, marriages and death dates. Mourning pictures featuring inscribed tombs, urns, mourners and willow trees often were made to commemorate a recently deceased family member, local hero or national figure.

The 1828 edition of *Webster's Dictionary* describes "work" in one definition as "Embroidery: flowers or figures wrought with the needle." More accomplished young women embroidered or "workt" bedhangings, tablecovers, blankets, pillows, upholstery, clothing, pockets and pocketbooks in white candlewick, colored silk and linen, and worsted yarns called crewel. Favorite motifs included flowers, scrolling vines, trees, animals and figures.

Tapestry and stumpwork embroidery, popular in 16th- and 17th-century England, was used to illustrate royal figures, as well as stories from the Bible or Greek mythology. Characters, buildings, trees and flowers—woven and embroidered with silk, gold and silver yarns—were often worked in relief on raised foundations called "stumps" which were pad-

Needlework

Infant booties, c. 1870. Makers unknown, United States. Wool embroidered with silk twist yarn.

Alphabet needlework sampler, 1824. Cornelia Bates, Ludlow, Vt. Silk thread embroidered on linen fabric. Gift of Theodore and Joanna Foulk. (8.2-85)

Embroidered picture, 1839. Maker unknown, marked "S.S.," Marlboro, N. H. Linen thread embroidered on wool fabric. Gift of Murphy and Jeanette Berger, in memory of their daughter, Susan J. Webster. (8.2-97)

ornamented with carved wood, wax, glass beads, ivory, fabric and lace.

Pictures made entirely of colored glass beads were also popular at this time.

Lace, tape and trims were essential costume accessories. Bobbin and needle laces, imported from England, France, Ireland and Flanders, were used for caps, shawls, collars and cuffs, while American women made endless varieties of knit, crocheted and tatted trims to decorate tablelinens, towels, bedcovers and clothing.

Exhibits in the Hat and Fragrance Textile Gallery are arranged by the needlework technique and focus primarily on samplers, lace, embroidered pictures and accessories, and needlework tools. Much of the earliest needlework including bedhangings, embroidered bead and stumpwork pictures and boxes are exhibited in the 18th-century Prentis House. Other historic houses contain numerous examples of schoolgirl samplers, embroidered pictures and decorative accessories.
C.Y.O.

Exhibited in: Electra Havemeyer Webb Memorial, Hat and Fragrance Textile Gallery, Historic Houses, Weaving Shop, Webb Gallery, Variety Unit

La Répétition au foyer, c. 1875. Edgar Degas. Oil and tempera on canvas. Gift of Electra Webb Bostwick. (27.3.1-35A)

Brazilian Hummingbirds, 1866. Martin Johnson Heade. Oil on canvas. (27.1.5-21)

The Death Struggle, 1845. Charles Deas. Oil on canvas. (27.1.5-18)

For centuries oil painting has been considered one of the highest forms of artistic expression. Paintings record the changing tastes, beliefs and values of human history. Portraits, landscapes and scenes of everyday life help us to understand both how the world looked and how our ancestors looked at the world.

Shelburne Museum's painting collection includes both European and American art. The European paintings are displayed in the Electra Havemeyer Webb Memorial Building and include works by Rembrandt van Rijn, Edouard Manet and Claude Monet. These were originally collected by Henry O. and Louisine Havemeyer, the parents of Museum founder Electra Havemeyer Webb. The Havemeyers were among the first serious American collectors of French Impressionist painting and built what is considered today to be one of the most important groups of Old Master and Impressionist paintings in the United States.

The French artist Edouard Manet (1832-1883) felt strongly that keen observation made a great painter. A brilliant technician who used broad strokes of paint as comfortably as he did minute dabs of color, Manet explored ideas about light that set the stage for the Impressionist movement. He completed the canvas *Blue Venice* while touring Italy in 1874. His dashes of paint create the effect of sunlight sparkling on water; on the gondolier, Manet uses multiple strokes of color to create a three-dimensional effect.

Claude Monet (1840-1926), a prominent leader of the Impressionist movement, stressed the importance of working outdoors and letting art illustrate the color and movement of the natural environment. Five landscapes by Monet are located in the Memorial Building. In the 1880s and 1890s Monet captured the changing effects of natural light by creating groups of paintings of the same subject in different weather and light conditions. His *Haystacks in the Snow* is part of a series of over thirty paintings of haystacks.

The Webb Gallery houses the Museum's collection of American painting, including both academically trained painters like Fitz Hugh Lane, Martin Johnson Heade and Andrew Wyeth, as well as untrained, or folk, painters like Erastus Salisbury Field and Anna Mary Robertson Moses (Grandma Moses).

Heade (1819-1904) was interested in science as well as the fine arts and painted images of tropical hummingbirds while traveling in South America in the 1860s. He recorded highly specific details in his canvas *Brazilian Hummingbirds*, including the shape

Six Rams, c. 1945.
Carl Rungius. Oil on
canvas. Gift of
William and Marie
Beach. (27.1.5-67)

*New York Yacht
Club Regatta*, c.
1856. Fitz
Hugh Lane. Oil
on canvas.
(27.1.4-69)

Penn's Treaty with the Indians, c. 1840-1845. Edward Hicks.
Oil on canvas. (27.1.6-1)

P A I N T I N G S

and color of tropical foliage and the shimmering plumage of different species of hummingbirds.

Unlike Heade, Erastus Salisbury Field (1805-1900) did not travel to Rome or Paris for extensive artistic training; in fact he never ventured far from his home in Massachusetts. Today, Field is classified as a folk painter. Field's masterpiece of color and imagination, *The Garden of Eden*, was one of several with biblical themes that he painted after orders for portraits dwindled because of the growing popularity of photography.

Several Vermont portraits and landscapes are located on the lower level of the Webb Gallery. Itinerant painters traveled around the state painting members of the growing middle class. In their desire to illustrate their new prosperity, many of Vermont's 19th-century merchants, lawyers, innkeepers and farmers commissioned portraits to hang in their parlors. Several portraits by itinerant artists are also displayed in the Museum's historic houses.

Paintings of wildlife, sporting scenes and American landscapes, located in the Beach Gallery, include works by Arthur Fitzwilliam Tait, Sydney Laurence and Carl Rungius. Laurence (1865-1940) was fascinated by the enormous splendor of Alaska. He first journeyed there in 1906 to paint and to prospect for gold and would eventually complete over forty canvases of Mt. McKinley. Rungius (1869-1959) made a career painting the wildlife of both the United States and Canada. President Theodore Roosevelt, who sometimes hunted with the artist, called Rungius' work "the most spirited animal painting I have ever seen."

The Pleissner Gallery houses the Museum's extensive collection of work by the artist Ogden Pleissner (1905-1983). Most well known for his hunting and fishing scenes, Pleissner also worked as a war correspondent, and painted landscapes in the U.S., France, Canada and Bermuda. The variety of work in the collection, from sketches and studies to finished paintings, as well as the entire contents of Pleissner's studio (which were moved to the Museum from Manchester, Vermont), offer the opportunity to examine the process of how one artist made art.
L.B.H.

Exhibited in: Beach Gallery, Electra Havemeyer Webb Memorial Building, Historic Houses, Pleissner Gallery, Webb Gallery

Footed bowl, early 18th century. Maker unknown, probably English. Pewter. Gift of Katharine Prentis Murphy. (35.3-276)

Detail of touchmark, plate, c. 1790. Nathaniel Austin, Charlestown, Mass. Pewter. (35.3A-107)

Porringer, 1791. Richard Lee, Springfield, Vt. Pewter. Gift of Dr. and Mrs. Fletcher McDowell. (35.3A-128)

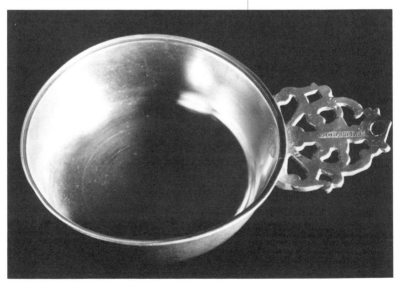

P ewter was widely used by the American middle class for a variety of kitchen implements and tablewares until the mid-19th century. The best quality pewter was almost entirely formed from pure tin, but small amounts of copper or antimony were sometimes added to strengthen the metal. Lower quality, less expensive pewter, used for chamber pots and undecorated plates, usually contained sizable quantities of lead.

Shelburne's pewter collections offer an overview of French, German, Dutch, English and American styles. Settlers brought pieces of pewter with them from abroad and many American merchants sold foreign pewter in their shops. It cost less than other metals, and in Europe its styles frequently copied popular silver styles. American artisans often relied on imported English and German pewter for stylistic inspiration. In fact, long after pewter had fallen out of fashion in Europe it was still being widely produced in America.

In the late 18th century, most American pewterers had emigrated from England. Trained in the proper handling techniques for metals, they sometimes also served as a town's silversmith or blacksmith. Because European tin exports were strictly regulated, and because tin was not widely mined in the colonies, American pewterers often resorted to melting down old or damaged pieces of pewter and reforming them into new objects. The relatively soft quality of pewter allowed it to be molded, remolded or spun (turned on a lathe) into a variety of forms such as teapots, candlesticks, plates and tankards.

Several examples of Vermont-made pewter are exhibited in the Dutton House. Pieces by Richard Lee of Springfield (active 1802-1820), and Ebenezer Southmayd (1775-1831) of Castleton, illustrate the variety of forms available in non-urban areas. To identify their work, American craftspeople used touchmarks similar to European marks or simply impressed their names into the pieces.

In the early 19th century, competition from imported porcelain, glass and pottery caused a dramatic reduction in the demand for pewter. In response, pewterers developed Britannia ware. Britannia, an alloy that increased the ratio of antimony to tin, was much stronger than pewter and could be turned on a lathe or rolled into sheets. It was also brighter than pewter and allowed the craftsperson to form more ornate shapes and styles. Several pieces of Britannia may be seen in the Variety Unit.
L.B.H.

Exhibited in: Dutton House, Prentis House, Variety Unit

The Old Farm House, 1872. Published by Currier & Ives. Lithograph with watercolor on paper. Gift of Rush Taggart. (27.6.8-218)

Blue Boat on the St. Anne, 1958. Ogden Pleissner. Watercolor on paper. Bequest of Ogden Pleissner. (27.22.3-195)

Eagle, mid-19th century. J. W. Prouty, Wilmington, Vt. Pen and ink on paper. (27.9-11)

Because they were inexpensive and involved little in the way of supplies, more works on paper—including watercolors, prints and pastels—were bought or created by Americans than painting and sculpture. Many of the techniques for creating art on paper were formally taught. Refined young ladies were tutored in watercolor painting, while young men were taught to handle a pen by drawing elaborate, calligraphic animals in ink. At home, inexpensive prints of landscapes, fashions of the day and portraits of statesmen decorated formal parlors and private chambers.

Shelburne's collection of twenty-eight thousand watercolors, prints, and pastels ranges in date from 1760 to the 1950s and includes everything from images of maple sugaring to French Impressionist pastels. Often used to interpret other areas of the Museum, the paper collection is displayed in most of the exhibit buildings. For example, images of children at play hang near the dolls in the Variety Unit, and prints of lake battles and maps are displayed in the Lighthouse.

Watercolor, the quickest drying and most transparent paint medium, was favored by many artists for portraits and landscapes and outdoor scenes. Shelburne's watercolor collection spans three centuries and includes American folk portraits, Pennsylvania-German frakturs and a set of rare, English costume studies. The 20th-century artist Ogden Minton Pleissner (1905-1983), whose work is exhibited in the Pleissner Gallery, was known for his watercolors of hunting and fishing scenes and used a special paintbox and small easel for painting from his canoe.

Prints, which are created by using a press and metal plate system, made possible the production of multiple copies of the same image. In late 18th-century America, the local silversmith with a talent for engraving on metal often worked with the town printer to produce printed pictures for the general public. Letterpresses and printing procedures are demonstrated in the Museum's Printing Shop.

Later, some artists hired printmakers to translate their work into printed form. John James Audubon (1785-1851) spent years traveling across America painting detailed watercolors of native bird species. He then gave his watercolors to an engraver for reproduction. The result was the monumental book *Birds of America*, completed in 1838, which featured handcolored engravings based on Audubon's watercolors. A selection of Audubon engravings is displayed in the Dorset House.

In the second half of the 19th century, the development of lithography allowed enterprising businesses like Currier & Ives to offer images for as little

PRINTS, DRAWINGS & WORKS ON PAPER   121

Louisine W. Havemeyer, 1896. Mary Cassatt. Pastel on paper. Gift of J. Watson Webb, Jr. (27.3.1-19)

Christmas Morning, 1943. Asa Cheffetz. Wood engraving on paper. Gift of Mrs. Asa Cheffetz. (27.6.13-36)

Common American Swan, 1838. Engraved by Robert Havell after John James Audubon. Engraving with watercolor on paper. (27.6.1.1-58)

PRINTS, DRAWINGS & WORKS ON PAPER

as seventy-five cents each. This development greatly expanded the American market for works of art on paper. Images by Currier & Ives, including hunting scenes, landscapes and portraits, may be seen in several exhibit buildings including the Webb Gallery, Lighthouse and Beach Gallery.

Pastels, soft chalks perfected by the French, were used almost exclusively for portraits until the late 19th century. The pastel collection at Shelburne includes 18th-century American portraits as well as masterpieces by French Impressionists Edouard Manet, Edgar Degas and Mary Cassatt. Cassatt (1844-1926), whose work hangs in the Electra Havemeyer Webb Memorial Building, was born in Philadelphia but lived most of her life in Paris and was an important part of the Impressionist movement. Cassatt's use of unexpected colors can be seen in the pastel portrait of her friend Louisine Havemeyer, mother of Shelburne Museum founder Electra Havemeyer Webb. In this portrait, Cassatt successfully used blue, green and even orange on the sitter's face and arms to create the reflective quality of skin. Outstanding pastels by Degas and Manet may also be seen in the Memorial Building.
L.B.H.

Exhibited in: Beach Gallery, Dorset House, Electra Havemeyer Webb Memorial Building, Historic Houses, Lighthouse, Pleissner Gallery, Printing Shop, Schoolhouse, Variety Unit, Webb Gallery

Prints, Drawings & Works on Paper

Mariner's compass with hickory leaf medallion quilt, c. 1830-1840s. Maker unknown, found in New Jersey. Pieced, appliquéd and quilted cotton. (10-22)

Mother and child detail, Haskins Crazy Quilt, c. 1870-1880s. Mrs. Samuel Glover Haskins, Granville, Vt. Pieced, appliquéd and embroidered cotton and wool. (10-215)

"Floral Medallion and Lion Cornerblock" doublecloth coverlet, 1840. Woven by Harry Tyler for Ruth C. Clarke, Palmyra, N.Y. White cotton and blue wool yarns. (10-420)

Embroidered bedrugs and blankets, coverlets, and quilts were a critical necessity in poorly heated early American homes. The making of bedcovers provided women with an important creative outlet and often served as the primary source of decoration in sparsely furnished 17th- and 18th-century homes. As America's economy grew in the 19th century, the increase in leisure time and the availability of inexpensive factory-woven cloth encouraged thousands of women to embroider, sew and quilt bedcovers for their families and friends.

Shelburne Museum founder Electra Havemeyer Webb was a pioneer in the appreciation of American bedcovers and among the first to exhibit them as works of textile art. She was attracted by the bold graphic patterns, clarity of line, intense colors, and the imaginative combinations of human figures, animals and vegetation, often whimsical and out of scale.

The still-growing collection she began at Shelburne is remarkable in its size and quality. Over seven hundred quilts, coverlets, blankets and bedrugs made in 18th- and 19th-century America illustrate the different types of bedcovers, the diversity of designs and fabrics, and the many methods of manufacture used by creative men and women. Although the collection predominantly represents New England and the northern states, it also includes examples from the southern and mid-western regions as well as from such distinctive groups as the Amish, Pennsylvania Dutch and native Hawaiians. The largest exhibit of bedcovers may be seen at the Hat and Fragrance Textile Gallery, while other examples are exhibited in the Weaving Shop and historic houses. Bedcovers made or used in Vermont, including a rare bedrug, are on exhibit in the Dutton House.

Bedrugs, a traditional northern European bedcover, were brought to America from northern England and widely used until the early 19th century. Now quite rare, these thick, heavy bedcovers were embroidered with handspun and dyed yarns on wool fabric to create a dense pile surface similar to that of an Oriental rug.

Handwoven blankets, treasured for their warmth and durability, often were embroidered with colorful handspun wool yarns. Women embroidered swirling vine, floral and shell patterns on plain blankets and filled squares of "window pane"-checked blankets with stars and flowers.

Single and double coverlets, handwoven in bold geometric patterns from the mid-18th to mid-19th centuries, were considered more decorative than plain or plaid blankets. While most were woven in

Quilts and Bedcoverings

Detail, trilobe flowers and clipper ships quilt, c. 1840-1850s. Maker unknown, possible New England. Pieced, quilted and trapunto cotton. Gift of Electra Havemeyer Webb. (10-21)

Trilobe flowers and clipper ships quilt, c. 1840-1850s. Maker unknown, possibly New England. Pieced, quilted and trapunto cotton. Gift of Electra Havemeyer Webb. (10-21)

Bedrug, 1819. Dorothy Seabury, Stowe, Vt. Wool yarn embroidered on wool fabric. Gift of Robert J. Whiting. (10-615)

QUILTS AND BEDCOVERINGS

blue and white, some weavers chose to emphasize the patterns by combining two or more colors. Jacquard coverlets, introduced in the early 19th century, became immediatley popular because of their elaborate floral, mosaic, figural and patriotic patterns. Professional weavers advertised them as "fancy" coverlets to differentiate them from handwoven coverlets with geometric patterns. The different patterns, colors, design motifs and weave constructions can be examined in the Hat and Fragrance Textile Gallery.

Quilts are made by joining layers of cloth—usually a decorative top, warm filling of either raw wool or cotton, and plain backing—and sewing or "quilting" them together. The method by which the quilt top is made—pieced, appliquéd or plain—determines the nature of the design.

The first quilts made in America followed English and European traditions. Early plain wholecloth quilts were made from lengths of imported, highly glazed, richly colored wool fabric. The stitches used to secure the layers followed decorative swirling vine and floral patterns similar to those used in embroidery or in painted decorations on furniture and walls.

The earliest pieced quilts were made by sewing or "piecing" small geometric pieces of fabric together in simple honeycomb or triangle patterns. As American women perfected the art of quilt making in the early 19th century, they developed more complex patterns often requiring hundreds and thousands of tiny pieces. Geometric star, flower, and figural patterns were pieced together in small blocks and then sewn together to make a quilt top.

The first American appliquéd quilts, made in the 18th century, used the *broderie perse* (French for Persian embroidery) technique of cutting entire motifs from imported printed fabric, then sewing them on a plain fabric background. Nineteenth-century quilters continued this tradition adding their own twists; they followed patterns printed in ladies' magazines, copied from a friend, or designed their own.

Occasionally women also stenciled, painted and embroidered fabrics to imitate elaborate quilt or coverlet patterns. Other bedcovers were knitted or crocheted in elegant patterns.
C.Y.O.

Exhibited in: Dutton House, Hat and Fragrance Textile Gallery, Prentis House, Sawyer's Cabin, Stencil House, Stone Cottage, Weaving Shop

Quilts and Bedcoverings

Interior view, stationmaster's desk. Railroad Station, 1890. Shelburne.

Railroad oil can. Date, maker and place unknown. Tin. (44.15-4)

SOMETHING NEW!

GRAND

EXCURSION

FROM

Shelburne,
Charlotte,
No. Ferrisburgh,
Ferrisburgh,
Vergennes,

New Haven,
Brooksville,
Middlebury,
Salisbury,

TO

SARATOGA

AND RETURN.

VIA

CENTRAL VERMONT

AND

DEL. & HUDSON R'DS,

THURSDAY, AUG. 19, 1886.

FARE FOR THE ROUND TRIP.

$1.50.

FOUR HOURS AT THE SPRINGS.

Races daily between the finest horses on the American turf.

Special Trains the Entire Distance will be run

ON TIME

AS ADVERTISED.

Persons desiring to remain over night and return on the 10.00 A. M. train next day, can do so by having their tickets exchanged at the D. & H. office, No. 1 Congress Hall Block, and paying $1.00 additional.

FOR TIME-TABLES AND FULL PARTICULARS SEE SMALL BILLS.

J. W. HOBART,   S. W. CUMMINGS,
G.M.C.V.R.R.   G.P.A.C.V.R.R.

Messenger Job Print. St. Albans, Vt.

Advertising print, 1886. Messenger Job Press, St. Albans, Vt. Paper and ink. (27.7.1-1)

RAILROAD EQUIPMENT & MEMORABILIA

Railroads brought great changes in commerce and communications to New England in the second half of the 19th century. Before the advent of railroads, New Englanders depended on the region's lakes and rivers and the sea coast as their primary avenues of travel. Traveling inland proved difficult over roads that were muddy in spring, dusty and rutted in summer and fall, and littered with tree stumps year-round. Beginning in the late 1840s, railroads brought new settlers to Vermont and helped the state's fledgling dairy industry flourish by providing access to markets for milk, butter and cheese. Railroads connected once-remote New England communities to the rest of the country, improving mail delivery and bringing newspapers from Boston and New York the next day instead of weeks later.

Dr. William Seward Webb, father-in-law of Museum founder Electra Havemeyer Webb, served as president of the Wagner Palace Car Company and the Rutland Railroad at the turn of the century. The Shelburne Railroad Station now at the Museum was constructed for Dr. Webb to serve the town and his estate at Shelburne Farms. Today it houses part of the Museum's collection of railroad equipment and memorabilia. The communication devices displayed range from the simple message hoops and "high-speed delivery fork," to technological innovations like the telegraph and telephone. Other items on display in the station include historic photographs and locomotive portraits, maps of the rail network in Vermont and the United States in the 19th century, broadsides and timetables for Vermont railroads, and models of early locomotives.

Manufactured by Dr. Webb's Wagner Palace Car Company in the 1890s, the rail car *Grand Isle* represents railroad travel at its most elegant. Prominent New York business tycoons traveled in their own private cars on business trips, or vacations to private camps in New York's Adirondack Mountains. Dr. Webb and his family traveled through the American West at the turn of the century aboard the family's rail car, the *Ellsmere*. The *Grand Isle* was a gift of the Wagner Palace Car Company to Edward Smith of St. Albans, Vermont, one-time governor of Vermont. When the *Grand Isle* was purchased for the Museum in 1960, its interior was refurbished to evoke the grand days of luxury rail travel.

Central Vermont Locomotive No. 220 was the last steam-powered locomotive used in regular service in Vermont. Built in 1915 by the American Locomotive Works in Schenectady, New York, No. 220 served on the Central Vermont Railroad until 1956, when the railroad presented it to the Museum.

Railroad Equipment and Memorabilia

RAILROAD EQUIPMENT & MEMORABILIA

Advertising print. Griffin and Winter, Publishers, Chicago. Paper and ink. (44.22-4)

Trunk, c. 1900. C.A. Malm and Co., San Francisco, Calif. Wood, canvas, leather, metal. (44.18-18)

Railraod lantern. Date, maker, and place unknown. Tin. (44.1-81)

The locomotive is known as "The Locomotive of the Presidents" because it pulled special trains for presidents Calvin Coolidge, Franklin Roosevelt, Dwight Eisenhower and Herbert Hoover during its tenure on the line.

The Freight Building exhibits a large group of railroad lanterns and glass globes from railroads around the northeast. Railroad lanterns served as a method of communication between conductors, brakemen, signalmen and engineers. Also in the exhibit are track-setting equipment, semaphore flags, hand cars, and other track maintenance equipment. The wooden replica of *Old Ironsides*, the first locomotive built by the Baldwin locomotive works, was first displayed at the Columbian Exposition in Chicago in 1893. Perhaps the most intriguing exhibit is the *Gertie Buck*, a self-propelled inspection car built and used by the Dewey family on the Woodstock Railway in eastern Vermont in the last decades of the 19th century.
R.M.S.

Exhibited in: Rail Car *Grand Isle*, Rail Locomotive, Railroad Freight Shed, Railroad Station

Leopard rug, c. 1880s. Maker unknown, New England. Wool rags hooked on burlap fabric. (9-M-36)

House hearth mat, c. 1780-1800. Maker unknown, New England. Wool yarn embroidered on wool fabric. (9-M-18)

Hooked and braided rug, c. 1860-1880. Maker unknown, New England. Wool and cotton rags, burlap fabric. Gift of Electra Havemeyer Webb. (9-G-13)

"Nevada" statehood tapestry, c. 1950. Molly Nye Tobey. Wool rags hooked on burlap fabric. Gift of Joel, Jonathan and Joshua Tobey. (9-M-82.28)

Carpets were a luxury in colonial America. Even the wealthiest Americans considered imported Oriental pile rugs too precious to walk on and used them as tablecovers. People found other ways to protect and decorate their floors. Painted patterns imitating tile, inlaid wood and stone were popular. Sand, used to scrub floors and absorb moisture, could also be sprinkled on clean floors, then smoothed and swirled into decorative patterns. Painted floor cloths, straw matting, needlepoint and some woven rugs also appear in household inventories. Rag rugs, then called "list carpet," were handwoven of colored fabric strips in random patterns across the width; "Venetian" carpeting was striped with densely packed, colored woolen yarns; and patterned rugs using overshot coverlet designs were made of heavy linen, jute and woolen yarns.

In the late 18th and early 19th centuries, English carpet factories began producing domestic Oriental rugs in floral medallion and geometric designs. These expensive Axminster, Brussels and Wilton carpets were imported and followed quickly by a more affordable variation called "ingrain" carpet, which became very popular. Throughout this time women decorated rugs with geometric designs, flowers, animals and human figures using needlepoint, shirring, "yarn-sewn" embroidery, braiding and hooking.

Shelburne's collection of over four hundred rugs dates from the early 19th through mid-20th centuries and focuses primarily on these handmade rugs. There are over three hundred hooked rugs in the Hat and Fragrance Textile Gallery, as well as numerous examples of embroidered, needlepoint, braided and woven rugs.

The earliest North American hooked rugs were created in maritime Canada and northern New England in the mid-19th century. The thick looped surface was made by pulling narrow strips of fabric through loosely woven cloth with a hook. The designs include simple geometric shapes, elaborate floral designs and scenes from everyday life. While many rug hookers designed their own patterns, others purchased printed patterns from individual manufacturers like Edward Sands Frost or the Diamond Dye Company, which distributed a mail order catalogue. Parallel to a renewed interest in early American crafts, rug hooking has flourished since the 1920s.
C.Y.O.

Exhibited in: Hat and Fragrance Textile Gallery, Historic Houses, Variety Unit, Weaving Shop

Pie crimper, c. 1840-1870. Maker unknown, New England. Carved and incised whale ivory colored with red wax, brass and silver. Gift of George Frelinghuysen. (37.1-15)

Yarn winding swift, c. 1840-1870. Maker unknown, New England. Turned and incised whale ivory and whale bone, wood padded with velvet. Gift of George Frelinghuysen. (37.1-122)

Sperm whale tooth, c. 1840-1870. Maker unknown, New England. Incised and inked whale ivory. Gift of George Frelinghuysen. (37.1-148)

The American whaling industry dominated the world market in the 19th century. It peaked in 1850 when seven hundred American ships with over twenty thousand men sailed from the South Pacific to the Arctic in search of whales. Voyages could last from three to five years, the ships returning only when their holds were filled with barrels of whale oil, processed from blubber. To pass the time aboard ship, a few talented sailors used whalebone and teeth left after processing, and more rarely baleen, to make homecoming gifts for friends and loved ones. With saws, files and awls they cut, turned, shaped and pierced the whalebone; with needles and knives they pricked and incised designs, which were then inked with lamp black or, more rarely, with colored inks. Sandpaper or sharkskin was used to smooth the ribbed teeth, and the sailors' hands gave the final polish.

While the best-known form of scrimshaw is the whale tooth decorated with engraved scenes, "scrimshanders" also fashioned shipboard tools, kitchen implements, domestic and needlework tools, and fashion accessories from whalebone and ivory. Tortoise shell, seashells, animal horn, pewter, silver and exotic tropical woods gathered during the whaling journeys sometimes provided decorative accents.

Shelburne's scrimshaw collection, exhibited in the Variety Unit, offers a broad range of forms. A variety of teeth are decorated with whaling scenes, portraits and patriotic motifs such as eagles and flags. A "Susan's Tooth," one of a handful engraved in the 1830s by Frederick Myrick aboard the ship *Susan,* is among the earliest documented scrimshaw still extant. Among the scrimshaw represented in Shelburne's collection are seam rubbers, used to crease the edge of a sail before sewing, and fids, large pointed picks used to separate strands of rope for splicing.

Pieces intended as gifts to wives and sweethearts include corset busks (inserted in a slit at the front of a woman's corset to firm the bodice), bodkins (small picks used to pierce holes in cloth or as hair decorations), pie crimpers, knitting needles, a butter print, a sewing box and a yarn winding swift. Baleen, the dark grey keratinous straining plates found in the mouths of krill-eating whales, often was used for commercial purposes but was rarely decorated. The large engraved piece of baleen on exhibit is unusual for its size and the intricacy of its overall decoration.
R.S.

Exhibited in: Variety Unit

Sternboard for the ship *American Indian*, c. 1785. Maker unknown, Salem, Mass. Carved and painted wood. (FS-13)

Eagle, c. 1875. Wilhelm Schimmel, Cumberland Valley area, Pa. Carved and painted pine. (FE-42)

Liberty, c. 1870. Eliodoro Patete, Anawalt, W. Va. Carved and painted wood. (FM-70)

George Washington on horseback, c. 1780. Attributed to Mr. Coolidge, Andover, Mass. Carved and painted wood, leather, and metals. (FM3)

SHIP & OTHER ORNAMENTAL CARVING

The Museum's collection of 18th- and 19th-century ornamental carvings, housed in the Stagecoach Inn, includes ship carvings such as figureheads, pilot house figures and sternboards; architectural carvings; and smaller decorative carvings meant for household use.

Shipcarving was an important adjunct to the burgeoning shipbuilding trade in 18th- and 19th-century America. Every major port on the East Coast supported shipcarvers whose shops stood side by side with those of sailmakers, ropemakers and other waterfront craftspeople. Shipcarvers learned their trade by apprenticeship with a recognized master.

The stock-in-trade of the shipcarvers was the figurehead. First intended to appease the gods of the seas, figureheads continued to represent ships' guardian spirits well into the 19th century. In addition to figureheads, shipcarvers also produced other ornamental work including sternboards, eagles for pilot houses and trailboards, and billetheads for the prow. Examples of these may be seen in the upstairs ballroom of the Stagecoach Inn.

As the shipbuilding industry declined in the mid-19th century, many shipcarvers applied their skills to other types of carving, especially trade signs, figures and architectural decorations. Perhaps the most popular image for carvers was the bald eagle, America's national bird and emblem for over two hundred years .

A number of different eagles may be seen in the Stagecoach Inn, including ship figures, architectural carvings used to decorate building facades, and several carvings by Wilhelm Schimmel. Around 1860, Schimmel immigrated to Pennsylvania's Cumberland Valley, where he made a meager living as an itinerant craftsman for the next thirty years. Carved eagles with crosshatching similar to Schimmel's were common in Germany in the Middle Ages, and he seems to have drawn inspiration for his bold, vigorous designs from this tradition.

Decorative woodcarvings also depicted other patriotic themes as well as a variety of familiar animals. Shelburne's collection includes small carvings of George Washington on horseback, a Revolutionary War soldier in uniform and a seated Lady Liberty, as well as several roosters, parrots and dogs and even a life-sized skunk whose raised tail probably startled a few household visitors.
R.S.

Exhibited in: Stagecoach Inn, Historic Houses

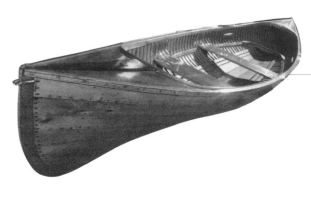

"Maryskiff" St. Lawrence River Skiff, c. 1885. Gilbert Boat Co., Brockton, Ontario, Canada. Wood and metal. Gift of Mr. and Mrs. Stephen B. Wiley and Michael Robinson. (40-B-10)

Pennsylvania rifle, c. 1800. R. Ashmore and Son, Lancaster County, Pa. Curly maple and iron. (43.2-39)

Shot holder, date unknown. "Am Flask and Cap Co." Tooled leather and metal. (43.2.a-16)

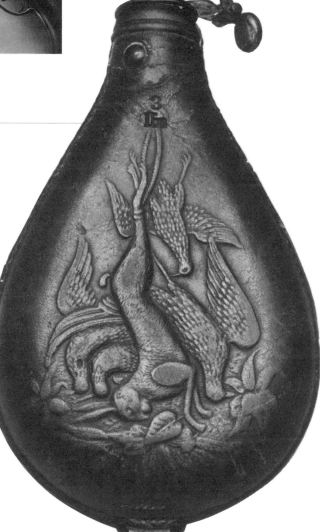

SPORTING EQUIPMENT

Among the foremost resources that distinguished America from Europe were its open lands and abundant wild game. As the American frontier was replaced by farms and urban centers in the 19th century, hunting and fishing were no longer merely acts of survival. Now they functioned as commercial pursuits for professionals and as recreation.

Shelburne's collection of shotguns, rifles, small boats and other sporting equipment serves as a complement to its collections of decoys and hunting trophies. Duck hunting boats and guns are exhibited in the Dorset House while Native American birchbark canoes, Adirondack guideboats and a St. Lawrence River skiff may be seen in the Beach Lodge.

Shotguns used to hunt wildfowl were loaded with small pellets of birdshot, while rifles used to hunt large game fired large single bullets. Double-barreled percussion shotguns, which loaded at the breech rather than the muzzle, were introduced in the 1840s and revolutionized wildfowl hunting. In addition to shotguns, commercial gunners who supplied city markets and restaurants with wildfowl sometimes used special guns to increase their kill. Two large-bore punt guns are exhibited in the Dorset House. These mammoth guns fired from 1 1/2 to 2 pounds of birdshot and could kill dozens of ducks at once. Also exhibited in the Dorset House is a homemade battery gun, consisting of seven shotgun barrels set in concrete. A trench below the barrels held powder, which when fired set the guns off in sequence, giving a wide and deadly spread of shot.

Fishing and hunting guides in upstate New York's Adirondack wilderness developed the Adirondack guideboat, a double-ended canoe-like craft with carefully beveled planking fastened with hundreds of tiny, rustproof copper tacks. Extremely lightweight, guideboats could easily be portaged by a single person; they were often fit with a shoulder yoke for carrying.

The meticulously restored St. Lawrence River *Maryskiff* represents a type of boat once ubiquitous in northern New York and Vermont waters. Originating on the St. Lawrence River in the late 1860s as guides' workboats, skiffs also were used on large bodies of open water, including Lake Champlain. The St. Lawrence River skiff was extremely stable and maneuverable, easy to row, and excellent for sailing, even though it had no rudder.
R.S.

Exhibited in: Beach Lodge, Dorset House

Sporting Equipment

Tenth anniversary umbrella and slippers, c. 1850-1880. Makers unknown, northeastern United States. Tinned sheet iron. (FM 187,188)

Basket, c. 1880. Maker unknown, northeastern United States. Tinned sheet iron. (35.11-45)

Presentation coffee pot, c. 1887. Maker unknown, New York. Painted tinned sheet iron. Gift of Henry Coger. (35.51.3-1)

The tinsmith was almost as important to early communities as the blacksmith. Using a variety of specialized anvils and shaping tools, the tinsmith crafted many useful items from inexpensive but reasonably durable tinned sheet iron. Many of the tinsmith's utilitarian wares were undecorated, but small boxes and coffee pots in particular often were covered with a ground of black asphaltum and painted with brightly colored geometric or floral designs. Tin lanterns, boxes and food-storage safe panels sometimes were pierced with an awl to produce decorative patterns that allowed light or air to flow through.

Shelburne's collections of household tinwares includes lighting devices, household implements, kitchenware and whimseys (fanciful objects). Many of these are exhibited in the Museum's historic houses. A number of unusual tin lighting devices, including a candelabra and mirrored wall sconces, may be seen in the Stencil House, which serves as a gallery for these and other decorative household furnishings.

A group of tinsmithing tools, including typically long and thin bickhorn and stake anvils, are exhibited in the Shaker Shed. The second floor holds a number of pierced tin lanterns, candlesticks and other tin lighting devices. Also on the second floor is an exhibit of tin whimseys, including a bonnet, a pair of slippers, an umbrella, a cane, an oversized bell and a pair of grain scoops pierced full of holes. These commissioned pieces were made in the mid- to late 19th century as humorous gifts to celebrate tenth or tin wedding anniversaries.

Exhibited with the whimseys is a tin cage for a pet squirrel complete with an exercise wheel, and a traveling tinker's "pig." During the early 19th century, traveling tinkers repaired tinware and other broken household metal objects. The tin shoulder case was used to carry tinsmithing tools and equipment from house to house. The circular hardwood "nose" of the pig sealed the case and also served as a portable anvil.

R.S.

Exhibited in: General Store, Historic Houses, Shaker Shed

Puzzle doll, c. 1875. Maker unknown. Wood with painted decoration. (22.1-99)

"Trick Dog Jumps Through Hoop" mechanical bank, patented 1888. Hubley Manufacturing Co., Lancaster, Pa. Cast iron with painted decoration. (22.4-10)

Clockwork circus wagon, 1870. Attributed to Stevens & Brown Manufacturing Co., New England. Tin, lead and iron with painted decoration. (22.5-62)

The impulse to play is universal, and throughout human history, people not immediately preoccupied with survival have found and created playthings. Toys of earlier eras offer important clues to the lives of their makers and owners.

Shelburne's collection includes both European and American toys that date from the beginning of the 19th century through the first decades of the 20th century, and encompass a broad range of both hand-made and manufactured examples. Although much of the collection is presented in the Toy Shop, playthings can also be found in the Museum's historic houses and the Variety Unit.

Simple toys such as marbles of clay or glass, and balls of cloth, wood, leather and rubber were available in homemade as well as more costly, commercially produced forms, and reappeared in new materials as manufacturing technology changed. Educational games from the late 18th century onward document the skills and subjects that children were expected to master. The profusion of commercially manufactured toys that appeared in Europe and America in the course of the 19th century attests to changes not only in technology, but in attitudes toward childhood and leisure.

Toys found in the American colonies included both local examples and the products of European manufacturers. Cottage industries on both continents produced wooden blocks, hobby and rocking horses, puppets, dolls and other simple toys of paper, cloth, wood and metal. After the Civil War, Americans found increasingly efficient ways to manufacture playthings and emerged as leaders in the manufacture of cast-iron banks; miniature boats and wagons of tin, cast iron, or wood; and lithographed optical toys and board games.

Although by 1900 America was a world leader in the manufacture of toys, people continued to make playthings by hand for a variety of reasons. Some toys, like whistles made from spring willow twigs or dandelion stems, simply could not be commercially produced. While homemade toys were often made by people who could not afford store-bought toys, even affluent friends and family members sometimes chose to carve a miniature cradle or a hobby horse, or to stitch a doll dress or a puppet as a special gift. Children also enjoy making toys, and the 19th century saw the rise of magazines and books with patterns and instructions for children's use.
E.B.

Exhibited in: Historic Houses, General Store, Toy Shop, Variety Unit, Webb Gallery

Merchants' and craftsmen's trade signs, c. 1850-1900. Makers unknown, northeastern United States. Carved and painted wood, iron and zinc.

Tavern sign, c. 1780. Maker unknown, New York or New England. Carved, turned and painted wood and wrought iron. (FT 55)

Tobacconist's figure, c. 1878. Thomas Brooks working in the shop of Samuel Robb, New York City. Carved and painted wood. (FT 34)

During the 18th and 19th centuries, trade signs advertised goods and services offered by craftspeople, merchants, and inn and tavern owners. Many early craftspeople promoted their wares with over-sized three-dimensional metal or wooden representations of the objects they made or repaired. A gunsmith, for example, might hang a large gun outside his shop; a dentist a tooth. Inns and taverns favored flat wooden signs that hung at a right angle to the building and usually combined an attractive painting with the proprietor's name. Often each side of the sign carried a different painting.

Although a few craftspeople made their own signs, most trade signs were the work of professional carvers and sign painters. During the 19th century, most major cities supported dozens of woodcarvers and sign painters. In 1881, Samuel Robb of New York, for example, advertised his firm's services thus: "Manufacturing of show figures and lettered signs a specialty. Tobacconist signs in great variety, on hand and made to any design. Ship and steamboat carving, eagles, scroll heads, block letters, shoe, dentist and druggist signs, etc."

Shelburne's collection of over 175 trade signs offers an extremely wide variety of forms representing dozens of different trades. Tobacconist figures, a favorite of collector Electra Havemeyer Webb, who bought her first cigar store Indian in 1907, fill the Stagecoach Inn's entrance hall and one of the downstairs rooms. A number of Shelburne's finest figures, including those of several other Indians and a snuff-pinching Scotsman, are products of the shop of Samuel Robb. One of these, inspired by the popular Civil War-era song "Captain Jinks of the Horse Marines," is a caricature of Robb in his National Guard uniform carved by Thomas White, Robb's partner of many years. Also in the Stagecoach Inn is an assortment of representational trade signs, including over-sized locksmith's keys, optometrist's eyeglasses and skatemaker's skates, as well as an enormous cobbler's boot, a haberdasher's hat, a clockmaker's watch, a carpenter's plane, a barber's razor and an innkeeper's pineapple, an early symbol of hospitality. *R.S.*

Exhibited in: Stagecoach Inn

French wallpaper, c. 1780. Maker unknown.

Stenciled walls of Stencil House parlor, early 19th century. Maker unknown, Columbus, N.Y.

Overmantel and chimney-surround, c. 1830. Jonathan Poor and "Paine," Maine. Watercolor on dry plaster. Gift of Saunders Manufacturing Company, Inc.

Nineteenth-century American homeowners used many methods to decorate plain interior walls. Rich paint colors, wallpaper, and decorative painting were all available in America as early as 1725. By 1830, thousands of trade painters offered wallpapering, mural painting, and stenciling among their marketable talents. Examples of all three types of wall treatments may be seen in Shelburne's galleries and historic houses.

The dining room of the Vermont House is papered with French wallpaper from about 1780. Imported French and English paper was purchased mainly by upper class residents of coastal, urban areas. Scenic papers were preferred for formal rooms like parlors, ballrooms and dining areas. This harbor scene may seem overwhelming today, but the bright colors and bold patterns retained their strong sense of design in flickering candlelight, a great advantage when one was entertaining in the 1790s. Other scenic wallpaper can be seen inside the entrance to the Variety Unit and in the Webb Gallery.

Also in the Webb Gallery is a painted overmantel and chimney-surround from a house in Maine. Painted around 1830 by Jonathan Poor and his partner known as Paine, the overmantel was part of a painted chamber featuring landscape murals. Poor traveled around Maine offering his services as a decorative painter and charged patrons $10 (about the same price as a good horse) for a completed room. The murals, with their views of busy harbors, farms and forests, are outstanding examples of a decorative technique that is frequently lost to demolition.

The wide-board interior walls of the Stencil House parlor, dining room and entrance hall are decorated with a variety of stenciled patterns, including a grapeleaf border, vases of flowers and patriotic eagles. In the early 19th century, artists traveled from house to house and stenciled walls in exchange for room and board. Stencil patterns were made from thin wood or heavy paper and could be used on walls or furniture. Look for examples of stenciled furniture and accessories in the Stencil House and also the Webb Gallery. Wall stenciling on plaster may be seen in the Dutton House, where fragments of original patterns found during restoration have been reproduced in the rooms and hallways.
L.B.H.

Exhibited in: Dutton House, Stencil House, Variety Unit, Vermont House, Webb Gallery

Mermaid weathervane, c. 1850. Attributed to Warren Gould Roby, Wayland, Mass. Carved and painted wood. (FW-47)

Swordsman whirligig, c. 1870. Maker and place unknown. Carved and painted wood. (FW-43)

Woman at spinning wheel tradesign and whirligig, c. 1850-1870. Salem, Mass. Carved and painted wood and iron. (FT 71)

The earliest recorded weathervane capped the Tower of the Winds in Athens one hundred years before the birth of Christ. Roosters, symbols of vigilance, topped bell towers of European churches throughout the Middle Ages. English settlers carried the tradition to America where vanes decorated public buildings and soon spread to barn roofs as proud democratic symbols of ownership and status. Farmers often proclaimed their trades by putting a homemade cow, pig or rooster vane on their barns while a wealthy horse breeder might top a stable with a finely crafted racehorse vane. Most of Shelburne's collection of 130 weathervanes are exhibited in the Stagecoach Inn.

Early vanes were often handmade for a specific location. The finest handmade vane in the collection is a wooden mermaid made about 1850 by Warren Gould Roby of Wayland, Massachusetts. The vane is remarkable for the strong, flowing lines of the body and billowing hair. Other handmade vanes include fish, Indian archers, a streamlined flying goose and a large and powerful standing wooden cock that originally stood on a barn near the Old Fitch Tavern in Bedford, Massachusetts.

In the latter half of the 19th century, several manufacturers offered hollow copper vanes. Because these vanes were made by hammering sheet copper into a cast-iron mold taken from a carved wooden pattern, the same form could be repeated many times. One of the downstairs rooms in the Stagecoach Inn offers a wide range of commercial copper vanes as well as a set of cast-iron molds for a racehorse vane and a unique wooden pattern for a large Lady Liberty vane. Many of the commercial weathervanes depict barnyard animals, including roosters, horses, pigs and cows; rarer forms include a centaur, a pouter pigeon and an anvil. One of the largest known commercial weathervanes, a highly detailed fire pumper pulled by a pair of horses, can be seen in the Round Barn. It originally topped a fire house in Manchester, New Hampshire.

A close relative of the weathervane is the whirligig—most often a standing figure with paddle arms that flailed in the wind. Some clever craftspeople built more complex whirligigs powered by a wind-catching wheel. Two of Shelburne's finest whirligigs, a paddle-armed swordsman and a woman seated at a spinning wheel, can be seen in the Round Barn. In the spinner, used as a trade sign, the woman's foot moved up and down on the treadle as the wheel was turned by the wind.
R.S.

Exhibited in: Round Barn, Stagecoach Inn

WEATHERVANES & WHIRLIGIGS

Weathervanes and Whirligigs

**Ladle,
c. 1840-70.
Probably New
England.
Wood.**

**Lidded bowl, c. 1840.
New England. Maple
burl. Gift of Katharine
Prentis Murphy.
(35.59.4-2)**

**Butter print,
c. 1875. Maker
unknown, probably
Pennsylvania. Carved
wood with turned
wood handle.
(35.5.1-15)**

The abundant forests of the Northeast supplied the raw material for most early American structures and objects. Wood was used for building, but also to make baskets, barrels, bowls, kitchen implements, furniture, tools from braces to hayforks, vehicle bodies and wheels, boats and more.

Among the most basic and common wooden objects were household utensils called treenware (*tree* plus *n*). Burls, extremely dense and hard scablike growths that form on tree trunks, were favored for bowls. The semi-circular burls often required little shaping to form a bowl. In addition to their strength, burls were often highly patterned with attractive grains. Bowls were formed by hand scooping or, particularly in later years, by lathe turning. Large groupings of wooden bowls, plates, spoons, ladles and other treenware may be seen in the pantry of the Prentis House and on the second floor of the Shaker Shed. Several large burl bowls also may be seen in the kitchen of the Dutton House.

During the 19th century, rectangular wooden molds, often with intricate handcarved designs, were used to form and decorate pastries and marzipan candies, while decorative prints, usually circular, were used to mark and identify butter from a particular home dairy. A large cakemold depicting George Washington on horseback, made by John Conger, a renowned New York mold carver, is exhibited in the kitchen of the Vermont House; other wooden pastry and marzipan candy molds may be seen in the Shaker Shed and the Stencil House. Several butter prints are exhibited in the Shaker Shed.
R.S.

Exhibited in: Dutton House, Prentis House, Shaker Shed, Stencil House, Vermont House

Woodenware

Plow plane, c. 1880. Sandusky Tool Co.,
Sandusky, Ohio. Boxwood, brass and iron.
Gift of Frank Wildung. (5.4.25-3)

Axe, c. 1800.
Maker unknown,
northeastern United
States. Wood and
iron. (5.1.1-8)

Sun plane, c. 1840-1880.
Maker unknown, northeastern
United States. Wood with iron
blade. (5.4.21-1)

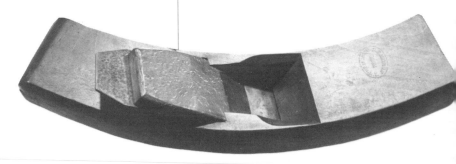

From colonial days through the mid-19th century, Americans depended on specialized craftspeople such as carpenters, joiners, cabinetmakers, and coopers (barrelmakers) who worked primarily with readily available native woods to provide essential goods and services to their local communities. Each craft required its own tools to perform specialized tasks.

Shelburne's extensive collection of woodworking tools encompasses a wide variety of both hand tools and machinery used by 18th- and 19th-century craftspeople. The bulk of the collection of woodworking tools is exhibited in the Shaker Shed. The work of early craftspeople may be seen throughout the Museum's exhibit buildings and historic houses.

Early settlers felled trees with axes and shaped timber with adzes to provide structural supports for their buildings. Heavy squared timber frames were connected by interlocking mortise-and-tenon joints, secured with wooden pins that, unlike iron nails, expanded and contracted with the frame. All of the Museum's historic structures are framed in this manner; unobstructed mortise-and-tenon framing can be seen most clearly in the second floor of the Horseshoe Barn.

The building trade was highly specialized in early America. Sawyers generally worked in teams to saw boards and planks from felled timber. Carpenters framed houses, laid floors and built staircases. Joiners did finer work, such as fitting joints, framing doors and windows, and preparing paneling, moldings and trim. Cabinetmakers, who employed many of the same skills as joiners, made chests-of-drawers, desks, tables and other furniture. Tools used by carpenters, joiners and cabinetmakers may be seen in the Shaker Shed; sawyer's tools are exhibited in the Sawmill.

Planes were the most specialized tools used by woodworkers. Dozens of different types were developed to prepare surfaces, fit joints and cut particular decorative shapes for moldings and trim. A typical joiner's or cabinetmaker's toolchest contained twenty to fifty planes, each with a specific function. Hundreds of woodworking planes are exhibited in the Shaker Shed.

Coopering or barrelmaking was an extremely important occupation in 18th- and 19th-century America. Coopers provided containers of all sizes— from small water and liquor kegs to 206 gallon hogsheads—for the storage and transport of goods including tobacco, whale oil, whiskey, molasses, flour, apples, sugar, and nails and other hardware. They also made water tubs, sap buckets, butter churns,

Woodworking Tools

Cooper's bung borer and tapered reamer, c. 1870. Manufacturer unknown, United States. Wood and iron.

Stairbuilder's trenching saw, c. 1880. Unknown manufacturer, United States. Wood and iron. (5.5.57-1)

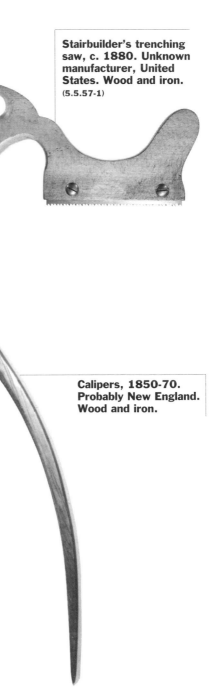

Calipers, 1850-70. Probably New England. Wood and iron.

milk pails, and drinking or ladling mugs called "piggins." The United States census of 1850 recorded forty-three thousand coopers. The introduction in the late 1800s of the metal drum and other machine-made containers for storage and shipping greatly diminished the demand for wooden cooperage. Today the craft is almost nonexistent. A complete exhibit of coopers' tools including froes, used to split barrel staves, and curved "sun" planes, used to shape the ends of the mounted staves, may be seen in the Shaker Shed.

The Shaker Shed also holds several pump logs and augers. Underground water pipes in early America were made of cedar or pine logs that had been cut while still green, hollowed out with special augers and fitted together. They linked supply sources such as springs or reservoirs with homes and businesses. Pump logs were virtually indestructible; some were still in use in Philadelphia as late as the 1950s.

R.S.

Exhibited in: Shaker Shed

ENTRANCE

Fine and Decorative Arts

Shelburne's fine and decorative arts collection represents the styles and tastes of 18th- and 19th-century America.

Fine arts collections include paintings, drawings, pastels, watercolors and prints. Whether landscape portrait, school study, or scenes from everyday life, these works supply a visual record of America's past.

Decorative arts refers to a wide variety of household goods including ceramics, glass, furniture and textiles. As America expanded, the growing market kept the nation's craftsmen and merchants busy and also attracted European trade. These objects help define an era when tea was always served from a pot, chair legs were turned by hand and wool blankets were produced by the town weaver.

Collections of fine and decorative arts of special interest are exhibited in these locations:

Beach Gallery
western landscapes and animal paintings, bronzes, and Adironack-style furniture

Dorset House
lithographs by John James Audubon

Dutton House
New England and Canadian furniture and American pewter, ceramics and textiles

Electra Havemeyer Webb Memorial
Impressionist and Old Master paintings, Chippendale and Tiffany furniture, and bronze sculpture

Pleissner Gallery
landscape and sporting scenes by Odgen Pleissner, and the recreation of the artist's studio

Prentis House
17th- and 18th-century furniture, textiles, glass, pewter and woodenware

Sawyer's Cabin
simple l9th-century furnishings

Stencil House
elaborately stenciled walls, l9th-century grain-painted furniture and decorative textiles

Stone Cottage
simple mid-l9th century furnishings and textiles

Variety Unit
pewter, glass, clocks, chalkware, English and American ceramics, and Chinese export porcelain

Vermont House
18th- and 19th-century furnishings

Webb Gallery
American folk and academic paintings, paint-decorated furniture, and works on paper

First coined in the 20th century, folk art is a term used to describe handcrafted objects made and used by ordinary people. Such objects were most often made by individuals who had learned their skill outside an academic setting; the best of their work exhibits a gifted understanding of color, line and pattern. The folk art to be seen at Shelburne Museum was made between 1780 and 1950, with the majority created during the 19th century.

In early America, fine art was available only to the more privileged classes. Some folk arts, especially portrait painting, imitated the academic traditions of European fine art. However, many American folk arts, such as quilts, decoys, stoneware, pottery, baskets and hatboxes, were created by traditional craftspeople to serve a specific personal or community need. Others, including weathervanes and whirligigs, trade signs, dolls and toys, were intended to be decorative, expressive or whimsical.

"My interpretation [of folk art] is a simple one," wrote collector Electra Havemeyer Webb in 1955. "Since the word 'folk' in America means all of us, folk art is that self-expression which has welled up from the hearts and hands of the people. The creators can be kin or strangers and they can be rich or poor, professional or amateur, but in America, and particularly in Vermont and all of New England, they are still known as 'folks'."

Shelburne's most important collections of folk art are exhibited at these locations:

Circus Building
carousel figures, circus wagon carving and miniatures

Dorset House
bird and fish decoys, and decorative and miniature bird carvings

Dutton House
paint-decorated furniture, and stoneware ceramics

Hat and Fragrance Textile Gallery
quilts, coverlets, hooked rugs, samplers and hatboxes

Shaker Shed
baskets, wrought iron, and tin whimseys

Stagecoach Inn
weathervanes, whirligigs and tobacconist figures

Stencil House
wall stenciling, paint-decorated furniture and accessories, and redware ceramics

Variety Unit
scrimshaw, stoneware and redware ceramics, and handmade dolls

Webb Gallery
paintings and paint-decorated furniture

New England Homes

Early New Englanders lived in homes as simple as log cabins and as elaborate as federal-style mansions. Most houses included a functional arrangement of rooms for cooking, eating, working and sleeping, designed for efficient living in the absence of good lighting, central heating, refrigeration and other amenities taken for granted today.

Beginning in the late-19th century urbanization and industrialization brought changes in the design and function of homes. Historic buildings were threatened. Some were torn down, others modified beyond recognition and still others abandoned to the elements. Museum founder Electra Havemeyer Webb saw the need to preserve New England's architectural heritage, and began collecting examples of 17th-, 18th- and 19th-century rural New England house styles.

Today the houses serve as exhibition space for collections of furniture and decorative and folk arts. Each suggests images of early New England homelife in a style similar to popular 19th- and early 20th-century perceptions—comfortable and welcoming homes supported by hard work and frugal living.

Dutton House
(Cavendish, Vermont, 1782)
18th- and 19th-century furniture and decorative arts

Prentis House
(Hadley, Massachusetts, 1733)
17th- and 18th-century furniture, textiles and decorative arts; exhibit designed by noted collector, Katharine Prentis Murphy

Sawyer's Cabin
(East Charlotte, Vermont, c.1800)
simple, rural furnishings

Stencil House
(Columbus, New York, 1790)
stenciled wooden walls; painted furniture and decorative arts

Stone Cottage
(South Burlington, Vermont, c.1840)
modest furnishings appropriate to a farm-worker's family

Vermont House
(Shelburne, Vermont, 1790)
high-style American furniture and decorative arts suggesting the home of a retired sea captain's home

Nineteenth-century America was a predominantly rural world with only one in nine people living in population centers with as many as twenty-five hundred people. Most Americans did farm the land, but our 20th-century perception of these small farms as being self-sufficient is not entirely true. Instead, most farmers also produced goods that could be traded for tools, skills, materials or cash.

By mid-l9th century the economy took bold steps forward. Improved design and production of tools allowed farms to become more productive. With the advent of mechanization, factories began to replace the home and artisan workshop. Children of farmers left rural settings to work in production shops, factories and mills, commerical enterprises, and service industries. By the 1860's, women as well as men secured positions in many of these work settings.

Shelburne's collections help to document this transition from farm to factory. Tool collections and recreations of work settings are exhibited at these locations:

Apothecary Shop
19th-century pharmacy and early 20th-century doctor's and dentist's offices

Blacksmith and Wheelwright's Shop
demonstrations in blacksmithing

General Store
1890s general store, tap room, barber shop and post office

Horseshoe Barn Annex
commercial horse-drawn vehicles

Printing Shop
demonstration in letterpress printing

Round Barn
agricultural tools, machines and vehicles

Sawmill
operating waterwheel and exhibits of early logging enterprises

Shaker Shed
tools of many early crafts and industries including woodworking, coopering, cobbling, and candle and saddle making

Weaving Shop
demonstrations of spinning and weaving

A pioneer family carting its belongings through the wilderness, stagecoaches rattling from town to town on deeply rutted roads, the gleaming brass and wood of the early railroads, and the steamboat's whistle as she approached a lake port: these are images of a New England society on the move through the 19th century.

Roads, rivers and lakes were the arteries of America's developing economy two hundred years ago. Rural settlers and merchants depended upon trade with the "civilized" world of America's cities and Europe to build their farms and businesses in early New England. Each development in transportation brought with it the promise of increased prosperity.

New Englanders saw great leaps in technology as they went from walking to riding on horse-drawn vehicles, steamboats and then trains. Now they could travel further, in greater comfort and at a higher speed than ever before. In 1791, it took the first settlers from southern New England over a month's hard journey on foot and by ox-cart to reach their new homes in Vermont. By the 1860s that same trip could be accomplished in one day by railroad.

Shelburne's transportation collections provide vistors with images of the ways New Englanders traveled by waterway, rail and road.

Beach Lodge
canoes and guideboats used on the lakes and rivers of Vermont and the Adirondacks

Lighthouse
exhibits of travel and commerce on Lake Champlain

Covered Bridge
Vermont's last surviving two-lane covered bridge with footpath, as well as wagons, omnibus and carriages

Horseshoe Barn and Annex
horse-drawn vehicles including sleighs, farm and trade wagons, carriages, children's vehicles, road and stagecoaches

Round Barn
agricultural vehicles

Ticonderoga
America's last side-paddlewheel passenger steamer with a vertical beam engine; exhibits of steamboat history

Steam Locomotive #220, Railcar *Grand Isle*, Railroad Station and Freight Shed
railroad lanterns, tools and memorabilia relating to Vermont railroads

Vermont was the last of the New England states to be settled and the only New England state not among the original thirteen of the new union, joining in 1791 as the fourteenth state. The first Vermont communities developed in the fertile Connecticut River valley and along the shores of Lake Champlain. By the early 19th century subsistence farming on homesteads had developed to commerical production on large farms that supplied New England with grain, potatoes and wool. Burlington, the state's largest city, had become one of the major logging ports in the country.

By mid-century Vermont's economy was caught up in the rapid industrialization occurring throughout the Northeast. To take advantage of the state's water resources, mills were built along rivers and streams to produce stoneware pottery, woven goods, carriages, furniture and machinery. New roads, railroads and shipping lines were built to link mill goods with markets in New England.

Lake Champlain, too, played a critical role in the development of Vermont. From the time of its "discovery" by Samuel de Champlain in 1609 through the decisive 1814 Battle of Plattsburg, the lake was of critical strategic importance. American Indian nations, France, Britain and the United States all vied for its control. Throughout the 19th century commercial traffic on the lake grew, and with the development of the railroads in the mid-19th century tourism emerged as an important regional industry. People traveled to Vermont, seeking health and relaxation at lakeside and mountain resorts.

Today Vermont's natural beauty and cultural wealth continues to draw travelers from all over the world. To better appreciate the region's history, visitors may wish to visit these exhibit buildings:

Community Buildings
Meeting House, Schoolhouse and General Store

Historic Houses
Vermont architecture and homelife: Dutton House, Sawyer's Cabin and Stone Cottage

Lighthouse
archeological, lighthouse and steamboat history

Ticondergoa
commercial lake history and steamboat exhibits

Round Barn
Vermont agricultural history exhibits

Webb Gallery
19th-century landscape paintings and prints depicting Vermont and works by Vermont artists

Shelburne Museum has been called a "place of the imagination." With exhibits ranging from a 220-foot-long side-paddlewheel steamboat and a turn-of-the-century steam locomotive and passenger car, to hundreds of dolls and toys and a miniature circus parade measuring over 500 feet long, young visitors with a wide variety of tastes and interests can find collections that delight. When small feet get weary, there is a turn-of-the-century carousel to ride and a family activity center in which to play. Owl Cottage Family Activity Center offers on-going activities that include playing with historic costumes and games, art projects, treasure hunts, self-guided tours, and quiet reading. Special programs welcome children to recreate wash day, experience the work of a printer's apprentice, and participate in l9th-century school activities.

Young Museum guests enjoy visiting exhibit buildings according to interests:

Dolls, Dollhouses and Miniatures
Hat and Fragrance Textile Gallery, and Variety Unit

l9th-Century Childlife
Schoolhouse, Sawyer's Cabin, Dutton House, Stencil House and General Store

Circus Collections
Circus Building and Carousel

Games, Toys and Children's Pastimes
Variety Unit, Toy Shop, Historic Houses and Carousel

The Great Outdoors
Beach Lodge

Transportation
Ticonderoga, Engine #220, Railroad Station and Freight Shed, Horseshoe Barn, Horseshoe Barn Annex and Covered Bridge

Museum Notes

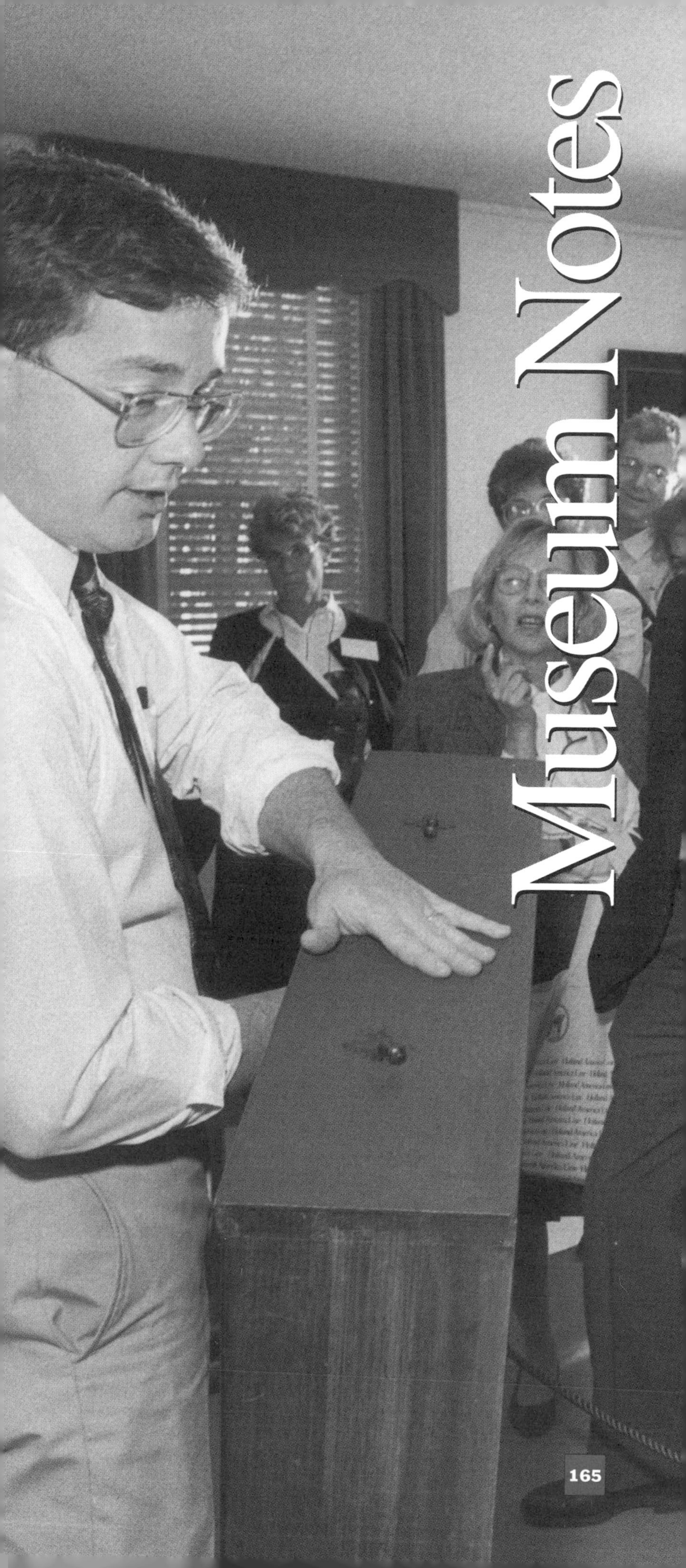

Conservation

Proper care of the collections is a major priority at the Shelburne Museum. The institution supports a modern conservation facility where professionally trained conservators utilize current practices to repair broken objects, arrest deterioration, and assure proper long-term care of historic and artistic works by monitoring and managing environmental conditions.

Repair of damaged objects involves scientific examination to determine the materials and processes by which the object was made; documentation of the object's condition; unobtrusive, aesthetically sensitive and fully reversible repair procedures and treatments; and a thorough description of conservation treatment.

Environmental care takes into consideration the setting in which the artwork or object resides. This includes regulating temperature, humidity and light levels within safe limits, and avoiding damage caused by other environmental factors such as dust, air pollution, insects, and animal pests.

Visitor cooperation in care of collections is most appreciated. Please be careful not to touch the objects in exhibit buildings. Damage can be caused by the oils that naturally exist on human skin, and accidental bumps against paintings can result in damage that is not always immediately visible and may be irreparable. Likewise, photography of light sensitive art works is restricted because of the damage that could be caused by extreme light conditions.

Shelburne Museum conservators participate in a variety of educational programs locally and nationwide, and are available by appointment to meet with Museum members and the public to offer advice on the care of personal collections. To arrange an appointment, contact the Chief Conservator.

Education

In keeping with the Museum founder's intent to "create an educational institution, varied and alive," the Shelburne Museum offers a variety of educational opportunities annually.

Shelburne's school programs serve close to one-third of the Vermont school population annually. Programs include workshops and small-group guided tours at the Museum, classroom presentations and the loan of artifact loan kits to school sites, and outreach programs to public libraries. Teachers benefit from a variety of continuing education programs and thematic tour and exhibit publications.

Area college and university students are served by specially designed lectures and tours in the fields of American art and history, education, recreational management and public relations. Internships are designed for undergraduate, graduate and post-graduate students in conservation, historic preservation, collections management and education. Stipends and intern housing are available on a limited basis.

Adults are served through a series of gallery and lecture programs, the annual two-day Richard H. McCann Symposium, spring and fall Elderhostel programs, and classes in traditional crafts. Outreach to adults includes speaking engagements at local historical societies and service groups as well as educational symposia nationwide.

Family groups can participate in special programs throughout the year. Saturday morning behind-the-scenes workshop programs are offered during the winter; and in the spring, summer and fall, daily activities are offered in Owl Cottage, the Museum's family activity center, where young visitors and their friends and family can participate in art activities, costume play, and historic games.

There is something of interest to everyone in the Museum's annual special events. "Lilac Sunday" offers a Victorian garden party atmosphere to celebrate the horticultural collections. "Farm Day" brings together craftspeople, musicians, theater groups, oral historians, farmers and horticulturalists to honor the agricultural traditions of New England. "Christmas at the Shelburne Museum" closes the annual calendar with a generous offering of musical performances and holiday activities reflecting both sacred and secular New England traditions.

For more information about educational programs, and to receive program announcements, contact the Director of Education.

Library and Archives

Shelburne Museum's library and archives are open to the public by appointment only. Library resources include nine thousand books related to the Museum's collecting areas, with particular strength in folk art, textiles, American decorative arts and Vermont history. Periodicals in the areas of museum studies, folk art, and American material culture and decorative arts are also available.

Archives, in addition to the Museum's own past records, include a small collection of manuscripts dating from the 18th, 19th and 20th centuries. These include letters, ledgers, diaries and certificates. Many items support specific collection objects; others provide a historical context for the collections.

The Museum's fifteen hundred photographs include Vermontiana and collections-related images.

To arrange a research appointment, contact the Director of Collections, Collections Department.

Membership

We invite you to join the growing number of members of the Shelburne Museum. Your participation assists the Museum in its important work of preserving a piece of America's past for the enjoyment of present and future generations. Membership dues help support general Museum operations including research, exhibitions, education programs and ongoing conservation efforts to preserve and interpret our nationally significant collections of art, architecture and artifacts.

Membership benefits include unlimited free admission; reduced guest rates; and discounts on Museum store purchases, workshops, and special events. Special mailings include a newsletter, annual report, and advance notice of all events. Members also receive free consultation from the Museum's curatorial and conservation staff.

For more information about Museum membership, please contact the Membership Office.

Gifts and Bequests

While admission fees provide a major source of funds needed to care for the collections and support educational programs and general operations at Shelburne Museum, gifts and bequests are needed to help maintain the high quality of the institution and its activities.

Gifts to the Museum help build and maintain collections; fund conservation efforts, exhibition research and interpretation; provide a broad range of educational programs and special events; and support projects not otherwise possible.

A gift or bequest can include a specific dollar amount, a percentage of an estate, or specified assets such as securities, real estate, or tangible personal property (for example, works of art or artifacts), that may be added to the Museum's collections or otherwise used for the benefit of the Museum.

All contributions made to Shelburne Museum are tax-deductible, as provided by law. Friends interested in discussing gifts to Shelburne Museum are encouraged to write the Executive Director.

Index

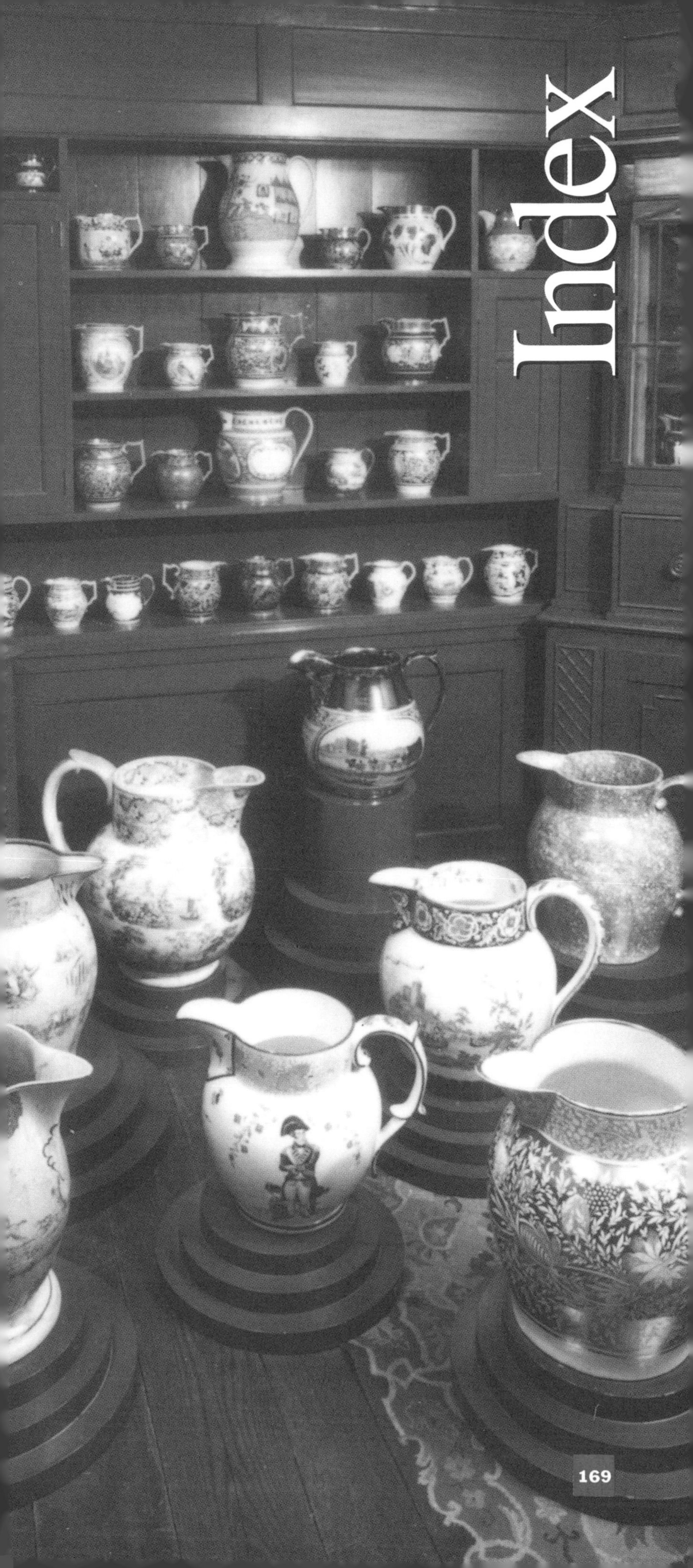

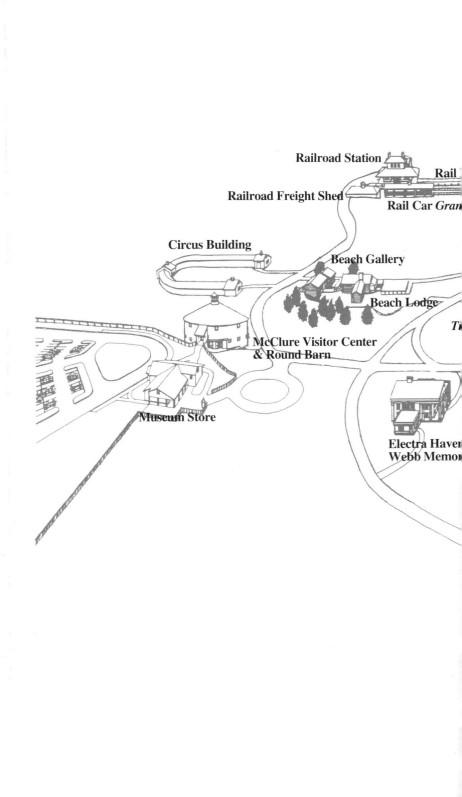

Railroad Station

Rail

Railroad Freight Shed

Rail Car *Gran*

Circus Building

Beach Gallery

Beach Lodge

Ti

McClure Visitor Center
& Round Barn

Electra Haver
Webb Memo

Museum Store

Map

Credits

Project Director Catherine Wood

Contributors
Eloise Beil
Marilyn Fish
Lauren B. Hewes
Garet Livermore
Celia Y. Oliver
Robert Shaw
Richard M. Strum
With
Holly Beardwood
Oda Hubbard
Sloane Stephens

Editor Suzi Wizowaty

Index Audrey Ritter

Photographs Ken Burris

Design Laura McCurdy

Cover images: (front cover, top to bottom)
mochaware, mid-19th century; Mariner's Compass
quilt, c. 1830-1840s; Dentzel carousel figure, c.
1895; *Louisa Ellen Gallond Cooke*, c. 1838, Erastus
Salisbury Field; green-wing teal duck decoys, 1948;
(back cover, top to bottom) interior view, Stencil
House, c. 1804; "Eagle on Uncle Sam's Hat" decorative carving, c. 1870; children's toys, 19th century;
Berlin coach, c. 1890.